Basic Algebra

by Jerome D. Kaplan, Ed.D.

EDUCATIONAL DESIGN, INC.
EDI 322

ISBN# 0-87694-240-0   EDI 322

Table of Contents

1. *Using Letters for Numbers*

1.1 Symbols for Numbers

Mathematics uses many symbols—such as

23 or 850 or 2096 for numbers
+ for add
− for subtract
× for multiply
÷ for divide

There are also special symbols such as $, %, and π.

Sometimes there are several symbols for the same thing. Here are a few symbols for multiplication:

$$6 \times 5 = 30$$
$$(6)\,(5) = 30$$
$$6 \cdot 5 = 30$$

- -

In algebra, we often use letters in place of numbers. We can use *a*, *b*, *c*, *x*, *y*, *z*, or any other letter. Any letter will do. Here's an example:

$$7 + m$$

means that 7 and some number that we are calling *m* are added together.

In this example:

$$13 - q$$

a number *q* is subtracted from 13.

To show multiplication with a letter, we usually omit the multiplication sign:

$$5y$$

means 5 times *y*.

- -

The letters that stand for numbers are called **literal numbers** ("literal" means letter) or **variables**, or, sometimes, **unknowns**.

You will often see two or more literal numbers together. This combination:

$$3abc$$

means the result of multiplying 3 times *a* times *b* times *c*, or $3 \times a \times b \times c$.

- -

✎ Exercises

What do each of the following mean? (The first one has been done for you.)

1. $7 + z$ _7 plus z_

2. $h - 5$ _____

3. $9 \cdot r$ _____

4. $a + b$ _____

5. $9xyz$ _____

6. $(7)(a)$ _____

7. $4r$ _____

8. $2a + 2b$ _____

What is the value of each of the following if $c = 7$? (Do the math.)

9. $3c$ _____

10. $6 + c$ _____

11. $\dfrac{56}{c}$ _____

12. $c - 7$ _____

13. $2c - 10$ _____

14. $4 + 3c + c$ _____

Suppose $c = 8$ instead of 7. What is the value of the following now?

15. $3c$ _____

16. $6 + c$ _____

17. $\dfrac{56}{c}$ _____

18. $c - 7$ _____

19. $2c - 10$ _____

20. $4 + 3c + c$ _____

5

1.2 Exponents

Mathematics makes use of many abbreviations. One common abbreviation is the one for repeated multiplication. Instead of writing

$$7 \times 7 \times 7 \times 7$$

we write

$$7^4$$

In this symbol, 7 is called the **base** and 4 the **exponent**. An exponent tells us the number of times we multiply by 7. We read this abbreviation as "7 to the fourth power," or simply "7 to the fourth."

Since $2 \times 2 \times 2 \times 2 \times 2 = 32$, we write

$$2^5 = 32$$

and say "2 to the fifth equals 32."

- -

When the exponents are 2 and 3, we usually say something different. If the exponent is 2, as in

$$5^2 = 25$$

we don't usually say "5 to the second equals 25." Instead, we say "5 **squared** equals 25."

If the exponent is 3 as in

$$4^3 = 64$$

we don't say "4 to the third equals 64," but "4 **cubed** equals 64."

When there is no exponent, we assume that it is 1. So $z = z^1$.

- -

EXAMPLES

Look at each example carefully until you are sure you understand it.

1. *dddd* becomes d^4, and is read as "*d* to the fourth."

2. x^2 is read as "*x* squared."

3. t^3 is read as "*t* cubed."

4. 5 cubed is the same as 5^3, or $5 \cdot 5 \cdot 5 = 125$.

5. $z \cdot zzz$ is the same as *zzzz*, which equals z^4.

6. $aaa \cdot aaaa$ is the same as *aaaaaaa*, which equals a^7.

7. b^2b is the same as *bbb*, which equals b^3.

8. $7gg \cdot hhhh$ is the same as $7g^2h^4$.

9. 3^3 is read as "3 cubed" and equals $3 \cdot 3 \cdot 3$ or 27.

✎ *Exercises*

Use exponents to write each of the following. (The first one has been done for you.)

1. $8 \cdot 8 \cdot 8$ _8^3_

2. *ssssss* _____

3. $bb \cdot bbb$ _____
(Hint: $bb \cdot bbb = bbbbb$)

4. $3rr \cdot qq$ _____

5. $10 \cdot 10 \cdot y \cdot y \cdot y$ _____

6. $7 \cdot 7 \cdot 7 \cdot wwww$ _____

7. $aa \cdot bb \cdot cc$ _____

8. $3 \cdot 3 \cdot 3 \cdot qqqq \cdot xx$ _____

9. x^2x _____

Find the answer to each of the following. (Do the math.)

10. 2 cubed _____

11. 2^5 _____

12. 9 squared _____

13. 4 to the fourth _____

14. 1^2 _____

15. 4^3 _____

How do we read these? (Write how you would say them aloud.)

16. a^2 _____

17. b^3 _____

18. x^4 _____

19. 17^2 _____

20. 27^9 _____

21. y^{14} _____

1.3 Order of Operations

Sometimes it is easy to get confused about which operation to do first. The order of operations is not clear. For the following example,

$$6 \cdot 7 + 3$$

do we multiply or add first?

Here is the rule to use:

Multiply or divide first. Then add or subtract.

According to this rule, the example above becomes

$$6 \cdot 7 + 3 = 42 + 3$$
$$= 45$$

Multiply first, then add.

In this example:

$$6 + 7 \cdot 3 = 6 + 21$$
$$= 27$$

We still follow the rule and multiply first, even though the $7 \cdot 3$ was written after the 6.

- -

If both multiplication and division (or addition and subtraction) appear in the same expression, then we do them in the order they appear. For instance:

$$12 \div 3 \cdot 2 = 4 \cdot 2$$
$$= 8$$

In this example, we divided $12 \div 3$ first, then multiplied the resulting 4 by 2.

✎ Exercises

1. $5 + 2 \cdot 7 =$ _____

2. $2 \cdot 7 + 5 =$ _____

3. $25 \div 5 - 2 =$ _____

4. $36 \div 9 \cdot 2 - 7 =$ _____

5. $12 + 50 \div 2 =$ _____

6. $100 \div 2 + 50 - 4 =$ _____

7. $24 + 12 \cdot 3 \div 6 =$ _____

8. $72 \div 9 \div 2 \div 2 =$ _____

1.4 Using Parentheses

One way to make sure that we understand which operation comes first is to use parentheses. Parentheses make it clear which operation to do first. We do the operation in the parentheses first.

Look at this example:

$$(6 - 2) \cdot 7$$

The parentheses tell us to subtract first, then multiply:

$$(6 - 2) \cdot 7 = 4 \cdot 7$$
$$= 28$$

- -

What is the meaning of the following example?

$$9\,(x + 3)$$

It means that the sum of x and 3 is multiplied by 9. Because $x + 3$ is enclosed by parentheses, we add first before we multiply by 9.

If $x = 4$, then

$$9\,(x + 3) = 9\,(4 + 3)$$
$$= 9 \cdot 7$$
$$= 63$$

The result shows that $9\,(x + 3)$ is equal to 63 when x equals 4.

- -

EXAMPLES

Again, look carefully at each example until you are sure you understand it.

1. If $a = 3$ and $b = 2$, then

$$2\,(a)\,(b^2) = 2\,(3)\,(2^2)$$
$$= 2\,(3)\,(2 \cdot 2)$$
$$= 2\,(3)\,(4)$$
$$= 24$$

2. If $x = 2$ and $y = 7$, then

$$4\,(x + y) = 4\,(2 + 7)$$
$$= 4 \cdot 9$$
$$= 36$$

3. If $r = 5$ and $s = 6$, then

$$4\,(r^2)\,(s + 2) = 4\,(5^2)\,(6 + 2)$$
$$= 4 \cdot 25 \cdot 8$$
$$= 100 \cdot 8$$
$$= 800$$

4. $(4)^2\,(3 \cdot 2)^2 = (4)^2\,(6)^2$
$$= (4 \cdot 4)\,(6 \cdot 6)$$
$$= 16 \cdot 36$$
$$= 576$$

5. $(3x)^2 = (3x) \cdot (3x)$
$$= 3 \cdot 3 \cdot x \cdot x$$
$$= 9x^2$$

✎ *Exercises*

What is the value of each if $x = 3$ and $y = 2$? (Do the math. The first one is done for you.)

1. $2\,(x + y) = $ _____ *10* _____

2. $5\,(xy) = $ _____

3. $6\,(x + y^2) = $ _____

4. $(x^2) - (y^3) = $ _____

5. $(xy)^2 = $ _____

6. $2\,(x^2 - y) = $ _____

7. $10\,(x^2 + y) = $ _____

8. $20\,(xy)\,(x + y) = $ _____

1.5 Expressions, Terms, and Coefficients

An **expression** is any group of numbers and variables. Here are some examples of an expression:

$$4a^2 + 8a + 7$$

$$34s^3$$

$$23r^2 + 45s^3 + t$$

A **term** is a special type of expression. The variables and numbers of a term are connected only by multiplication. Each of these is an example of a term:

$$4x$$

$$5y^2$$

$$17xy^2z$$

The expression $3x^4 + 5y^3 - 9z^2$ has three terms.

The **coefficient** is the number that comes in front of a variable.

The coefficient of $6x^3$ is 6.

The coefficient of $23z^2$ is 23.

Be careful of this one:

The coefficient of y is 1 (because $y = 1 \cdot y$).

✎ Exercises

How many terms are in each expression?

1. $4r^3 + 3r^2 + 23$ _____

2. $3s^5 + 9s^4$ _____

3. $12,356x^9$ _____

4. 0.2387 _____

What is the coefficient for each term?

5. $13x^3$ _____

6. $10a^2$ _____

7. r _____

8. $\dfrac{2}{3}x$ _____

9. $0.15y$ _____

Write the letter **T** next to each expression that has more than one term:

10. $6x + 7y$ _____

11. $3t^2 - 2t + 17$ _____

12. $64m - 7$ _____

13. $0.25r^3$ _____

14. $9j$ _____

15. $18 - 3x^3$ _____

1.6 Writing Expressions

A good deal of the work we do in algebra requires translating words and phrases into mathematical symbols, or expressions. For instance, when we hear "the product of 7 and *a*," we think "multiplication," and we translate these words into $7 \cdot a$ or $7a$.

If we hear "the sum of *x* and 9," we think "addition," and we translate into $x + 9$.

Here is a table of phrases that are used frequently, and how they get translated into expressions:

Phrases Meaning Addition

3 plus *y*	$3 + y$
add 3 and *y*	$3 + y$
increase *y* by 3	$y + 3$ (or $3 + y$—they're the same)
the sum of 25 and *q*	$25 + q$

Phrases Meaning Subtraction (Be careful. The order of items in the expression is important!)

z minus 8	$z - 8$
subtract 8 from *z*	$z - 8$ (*not* $8 - z$!)
decrease *z* by 8	$z - 8$ (*not* $8 - z$!)
t less 5	$t - 5$
the difference of *c* from 18	$18 - c$ (*not* $c - 18$!)
5 less *x*	$5 - x$

Phrases Meaning Multiplication

r times *s*	rs (or $r \cdot s$)
multiply *r* and *s*	rs
the product of *r* and *s*	rs

Phrases Meaning Division

divide *m* by 13	$\frac{m}{13}$ ($m \div 13$ is also correct, but the $\div$ sign isn't used much in algebra)
m divided by 13	$\frac{m}{13}$
the quotient of *m* divided by 13	$\frac{m}{13}$
m over 13	$\frac{m}{13}$

✎ *Exercises*

Write the expressions for each of the following:

1. the sum of 4 and t _____

2. the product of z and 7 _____

3. the difference of 23 from w _____

4. the quotient of 4 divided by g _____

5. 16 less b _____

6. increase m by r^2 _____

7. decrease 100 by s^2 _____

Translate these expressions into words:

8. $a + d$ _____

9. xy _____

10. $\dfrac{4}{p}$ _____

11. $17 + p^2$ (use the word "increase") _____

12. $33 - k$ (use the word "less") _____

13. $m - n^2$ (use the word "decrease") _____

GLOSSARY

This glossary covers words that you often need in algebra. These words are particularly useful in the next section on formulas.

Product—the result of a multiplication problem; 6 is the product of 2 and 3

Quotient—the result of a division problem; 2 is the quotient of 6 divided by 3

Altitude—the perpendicular distance from a **vertex** (point) of a triangle to the opposite side; also used with rectangles and parallelograms

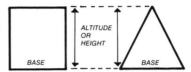

Height—1) another name for altitude of a triangle, rectangle or parallelogram; 2) the distance from the base of a solid to the top of a solid

Base—1) any side of a triangle, usually the side that is drawn horizontally; 2) the bottom of a solid

Perimeter—the distance around a triangle, square, or rectangle

Circumference—the distance around a circle

Radius—a line segment that connects the center of a circle to the circumference; the distance from the center of a circle to the edge

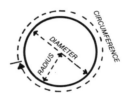

Diameter—a line segment that goes through the center of a circle and touches the circle twice; the distance from one side of a circle to the other

π (pi)—pronounced "pie," a number approximately equal to 3.14, or $\frac{22}{7}$

Rectangular solid—usually known as a "box"; it is a solid with all sides rectangles

Cube—a rectangular solid with all sides squares (and all edges the same length)

1.7 Formulas

The area of a rectangle is found by multiplying its length by its width. In symbols, the letter *A* stands for area, the letter *l* stands for length, and the letter *w* stands for width. So this statement looks like:

$$A = lw$$

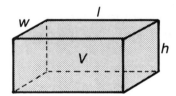

This statement is called a ***formula.***

If the length is 6 feet and the width is 4 feet, then the area can be found by using this formula:

$$A = lw$$
$$A = 6 \cdot 4$$
$$A = 24$$

The area is 24 square feet.

- -

Here's the formula for the volume of a rectangular solid (a box):

$$V = lwh$$

It states that to find the volume of a rectangular solid, multiply the length by the width, and then multiply by the height.

Suppose the length of a rectangular solid is 4 inches, the width 7 inches, and the height 9 inches. Then using the formula above:

$$V = lwh$$
$$V = 4 \cdot 7 \cdot 9$$
$$V = 252$$

The volume of the rectangular solid is 252 cubic inches.

- -

✎ Exercises

Write an expression for each of the following:

1. the sum of 8 and z _____

2. 3 less than w _____

3. the product of a and b _____

4. the quotient of 7 divided by t _____

5. 10 less than the product of x and y ___

Write the following as formulas:

6. The area of a triangle is equal to one-half the product of the base and the altitude. Use A for area, b for base, and h for altitude (or height). _____

7. The circumference of a circle is 2 times π times the radius. Use c for circumference and r for the radius. _____

8. The perimeter of a rectangle is the sum of all sides of the rectangle. Use p for perimeter, l for length, and w for width. (Remember: a rectangle has 4 sides!)

   _____

9. The area of a square is equal to a side multiplied by itself. Use s for the side.

   _____

10. The volume of a cube equals the length of the base times the width of the base times the height. Use V for volume, l for length, w for width, and h for height.

    _____

11. The volume of a cube equals the cube of the length of one of its sides. Use V for volume and s for the length of a side. _____

1.8 Adding and Subtracting Like Terms

When we add or subtract numbers, it doesn't matter what the numbers are—whole numbers, fractions, or decimals. We can add these numbers together. But if we want to add or subtract algebraic terms, we must make sure that the exponents and the variables are the same.

Look at these two terms:

$$6x^2 \text{ and } 7x^2$$

We can add or subtract these terms, since the variable x and the exponent 2 are the same:

$$6x^2 + 7x^2 = 13x^2$$

But in the case of

$$4x^2 \text{ and } 9x^3$$

the variable x is the same, but the exponents 2 and 3 are not. So we cannot add or subtract the terms.

When terms have the same variables and exponents, the terms are called **like terms**. (**Like** means "similar.")

- -

Here's the rule to follow when adding or subtracting:

We can add or subtract only those terms that are like terms.

And here's a warning rule:

To add or subtract like terms, add or subtract their coefficients only.

- -

EXAMPLES

1. We **cannot** add: $3y^2 + 2z^2$ because these terms are not like terms—they do not have the same variables. The exponents are the same, but the variables are not.

2. We **can** subtract $14t^3 - 9t^3$ because the terms are like terms—they have the same variables and exponents:

$$14t^3 - 9t^3 = 5t^3$$

3. We **can** add $12xy + 7xy$ because the terms are like terms:

$$12xy + 7xy = 19xy$$

4. For the expression:

$$3z^2 + 5z^2 + 2x^3 + 8x^3$$

the first two terms are like terms, and the final two terms are also like terms. Adding the like terms, we have:

$$3z^2 + 5z^2 + 2x^3 + 8x^3 = 8z^2 + 10x^3$$

Since order is not important in addition, we can also write the answer as $10x^3 + 8z^2$.

5. For the expression

$$14rs^2t + 3r^2st - 7rs^2t$$

the first and third terms are like terms. We group the like terms together (in parentheses) and then subtract:

$$14rs^2t + 3r^2st - 7rs^2t = (14rs^2t - 7rs^2t) + 3r^2st$$
$$= 7rs^2t + 3r^2st$$

✎ *Exercises*

Find the sum or difference for each:

1. $2x + 5x =$ _____

2. $12y^2 - 7y^2 =$ _____

3. $6m^3 + 2r^2 + 6m^3 =$ _____

4. $8xy + 4xy + 3x^2y =$ _____

5. $15ab^2 + 10a^3b - 5ab^2 - 3a^3b =$ __

_____

Put an **X** by any of the following expressions that **cannot** be added or subtracted:

6. $6a^3b + 2a^3b$ _____

7. $9xy - 4x^2y$ _____

8. $3ab + 2xy$ _____

9. $19abc - 13abc$ _____

10. $230x + 150x + 73x - 12x - x$ _____

_____

1.9 Multiplying Terms

To add or subtract, we have to be sure that the terms are like terms. But when we multiply, the terms do **not** have to be like terms. Look at this example:

$$(6x^2)\,(7x) = ?$$

Rearrange the two terms as shown:

$$(6x^2)\,(7x) = 6 \cdot 7 \cdot x^2x$$
$$= 42 \cdot x^2x$$
$$= 42xxx$$
$$= 42x^3$$

From this example we can see that one good way to multiply terms is to follow these steps:

Step 1: Rearrange terms to bring coefficients together and variables together.

Step 2: Multiply the coefficients.

Step 3: Multiply the variables.

EXAMPLES

1. $3xy \cdot 5y = 3 \cdot 5xy \cdot y$
$\qquad\quad = 15xy \cdot y$
$\qquad\quad = 15xy^2$

2. $2xyz \cdot 12xyz = 2 \cdot 12xyz \cdot xyz$
$\qquad\qquad\quad = 24xyz \cdot xyz$
$\qquad\qquad\quad = 24xxyyzz$
$\qquad\qquad\quad = 24x^2y^2z^2$

3. $(x^2)\,(2x^3)\,(3x^4) = 1 \cdot 2 \cdot 3x^2x^3x^4$
$\qquad\qquad\qquad = 6x^2x^3x^4$
$\qquad\qquad\qquad = 6xx \cdot xxx \cdot xxxx$
$\qquad\qquad\qquad = 6x^9$

4. $2a \cdot 3b^2 + 4a \cdot 5b^2 = 2 \cdot 3ab^2 + 4 \cdot 5ab^2$
$\qquad\qquad\qquad\qquad = 6ab^2 + 20ab^2$
$\qquad\qquad\qquad\qquad = 26ab^2$

5. $(5r^2s)\,(2rs^3)\,(3rs) = 5 \cdot 2 \cdot 3r^2s \cdot rs^3rs$
$\qquad\qquad\qquad\quad = 30r^2s \cdot rs^3 \cdot rs$
$\qquad\qquad\qquad\quad = 30rrrr \cdot sssss$
$\qquad\qquad\qquad\quad = 30r^4s^5$

✎ Exercises

1. $2z \cdot 3z = 2 \cdot 3z \cdot z = $ _____

2. $4xy \cdot 2x = $ _____

3. $(a)\,(a^2)\,(a^3) = $ _____

4. $2rs \cdot 7r = $ _____

5. $2mn \cdot 5m^2 + 3m^2n \cdot 7m = $ _____

6. $(19xyz)\,(xy^3) - (13xy^4z)\,(x) = $ _____

7. $3ab \cdot bc = $ _____

8. $(5q^2t^3v)\,(2q^3t^2v) = $ _____

9. $2x \cdot 3y + 4x \cdot 6z + 5x \cdot 7y = $ _____

10. $(3x)^2 = $ _____

1.10 Dividing Terms

Before we learn how to divide one term by another term, we should think back about how to divide using ordinary numbers:

$$\frac{4 \cdot 4 \cdot 4 \cdot 4}{4 \cdot 4 \cdot 4}$$

In this example we use the technique of cancelling the same number in the numerator as in the denominator:

$$\frac{\cancel{4} \cdot \cancel{4} \cdot \cancel{4} \cdot 4}{\cancel{4} \cdot \cancel{4} \cdot \cancel{4}}$$

Cancelling leaves a 4 in the numerator, so the answer is 4.

Now look at this example:

$$\frac{7 \cdot 7}{7 \cdot 7 \cdot 7}$$

Here is the cancelling procedure:

$$\frac{\cancel{7} \cdot \cancel{7}}{\cancel{7} \cdot \cancel{7} \cdot 7}$$

leaving 7 in the denominator. The answer here is $\frac{1}{7}$ (*not* $\frac{0}{7}$!).

- -

We use the same cancelling technique to divide variables, as long as the same variable is in the numerator and denominator. Look at this example with variables:

$$\frac{qqqqq}{qq}$$

Apply cancelling:

$$\frac{\cancel{q}\cancel{q}qqq}{\cancel{q}\cancel{q}}$$

leaving 3 *q*'s in the numerator. The answer is q^3.

- -

When you divide one term by another term, as in this example:

$$\frac{16x^3}{2x^2}$$

first divide the coefficients, then divide the variables. That is, first divide 16 by 2, then x^3 by x^2:

$$\frac{16 \cdot xxx}{2 \cdot xx}$$

Use cancelling with the variables:

$$\frac{16 \cdot \cancel{x}\cancel{x}x}{2 \cdot \cancel{x}\cancel{x}}$$

Cancelling gives us $\dfrac{16x}{2}$, which equals $8x$.

EXAMPLES

1. $\dfrac{q^5}{q^3} = \dfrac{qqqqq}{qqq}$
   $= q^2$

2. $\dfrac{14z^4}{2z} = \dfrac{7zzzz}{z}$
   $= 7z^3$

3. $\dfrac{36ab^3}{4ab^2} = \dfrac{9abbb}{abb}$
   $= 9b$

4. $\dfrac{24x^7}{3x^2} = \dfrac{8xxxxxxx}{xx}$
   $= 8x^5$

✎ *Exercises*

1. $\dfrac{w^4}{w^2} =$ _____

2. $\dfrac{33a^5}{11a^2} =$ _____

3. $\dfrac{2rs^3}{4rs^2} =$ _____

4. $\dfrac{100xy^4z}{25y^2} =$ _____

5. $\dfrac{24v^5w^7}{48v^2w^3} =$ _____

1.11 Chapter 1 Review

This test is a way to find out if you have mastered the skills of Chapter 1.

What is the value of each of the following if $r = 2$ and $s = 4$?

1. $(r^2 + s)$ _____

2. $2r^3 - s^2$ _____

3. $\dfrac{2s^2}{r}$ _____

4. $2r^2 + 3s^2$ _____

5. $\dfrac{s^4}{2r}$ _____

6. $\dfrac{(2r + s)^2}{s}$ _____

Simplify each by doing the operation.

7. $2m + 3m =$ _____

8. $\dfrac{9a^4}{3a} =$ _____

9. $(5t)^2 =$ _____

10. $(3x)(4x) =$ _____

11. $\dfrac{12a^3b^2c}{3a^2b} =$ _____

12. $3xy^2z + 2x^3y^2z + 4x^3y^2z =$ _____

Write an expression for each of the following:

13. the sum of c and 5 _____

14. 7 less than the quotient of x divided by 6 _____

15. the product of r and s _____

16. increase y by q^2 _____

Answer the following questions:

17. What is the coefficient in the expression $9x^2y$? _____

18. How many terms are in the expression $2m^2 + 1$? _____

19. What is the exponent in the expression $4r^3 + 7x + 1$? _____

20. The symbol π is approximately equal to— _____

a. x
b. 3.14
c. a^2
d. 6

2. *Solving Equations*

2.1 What Is an Equation?

You have worked with equations for a long time. Here are some examples that are familiar to you:

$$4 + 3 = 7 \qquad 19 - 3 = 16$$
$$7 \cdot 5 = 35 \qquad 24 \div 6 = 4$$

What is an equation? It is a statement that two quantities are equal, that the left-hand side is equal to the right-hand side. For the equation

$$17 + 6 = 23$$

the left-hand side is $17 + 6$ and the right-hand side is 23. As you can see, the two sides are equal.

- -

In algebra, equations often have variables in them. In the equation

$$x + 6 = 8$$

x is a variable that stands for a number. The equation states that this number plus 6 equals 8.

If x is replaced by 2, then the statement is true:

$$2 + 6 = 8$$

We call 2 the **solution** to the equation $x + 6 = 8$.

EXAMPLES

1. For the equation $y + 10 = 17$, the variable is y. The variable stands for a number. The equation states that this number plus 10 equals 17. The solution is 7 because $7 + 10 = 17$.

2. For the equation $14 - z = 8$ the solution is 6 because $14 - 6 = 8$.

3. The solution to $9x = 72$ is 8 because $9 \cdot 8 = 72$.

4. Look at this equation:

$$\frac{t}{4} = 3$$

If t is replaced by 12, then the equation is true. Therefore, the solution to the equation is 12.

Find the solution to each equation:

1. $x + 7 = 12$ (Think: What number plus 7 equals 12?) _____

2. $12 - y = 3$ (Think: What number subtracted from 12 is equal to 3?) _____

3. $7z = 35$ (What number, multiplied times 7, equals 35?) _____

4. $\frac{q}{6} = 4$ (What number, divided by 6, equals 4?) _____

5. $6 + m = 13$ _____

6. $b - 10 = 6$ _____

7. $14a = 14$ _____

8. $\frac{15}{n} = 5$ _____

2.2 *Solving Equations by Subtracting*

In the last chapter you solved several easy equations by using informal, commonsense math of the kind you can do in your head. But you need to use more formal, step-by-step methods to solve more complicated equations. Most of this chapter shows you techniques for finding solutions to such equations.

- -

When solving equations, the main goal is to get the variable on one side of the equation by itself. For example, in the equation:

$$x + 6 = 13$$

we want to get x by itself. The way to do this is to subtract 6 from $x + 6$. But if we subtract 6 from the left-hand side, we also have to subtract 6 from the right-hand side:

$$\begin{array}{rcr} x + 6 = & & 13 \\ -\ 6 & & -\ 6 \\ \hline x\quad\ = & & 7 \end{array}$$

By subtracting the same number from both sides of the equation, we are able to get x by itself: $x = 7$. The solution is 7.

For a check, replace x by 7 in the original equation: $7 + 6 = 13$. So the solution is correct.

- -

Now look at another equation:

$$z + 24 = 76$$

we want to get z by itself. To do this, use the same method. We subtract 24 from both sides of the equation:

$$\begin{array}{rcr} z + 24 = & & 76 \\ -\ 24 & & -\ 24 \\ \hline z\quad\ = & & 52 \end{array}$$

The solution is 52.

To check, replace z by 52: $52 + 24 = 76$.

✎ *Exercises*

Solve these equations and check your answers.

1. $x + 3 = 24$ _____

2. $t + 18 = 27$ _____

3. $k + 67 = 84$ _____

4. $m + 40 = 90$ _____

5. $5 + j = 13$ _____

6. $22 + y = 38$ _____

7. $z + 100 = 800$ _____

8. $n + 44 = 44$ _____

9. $56 + x = 72$ _____

10. $r + 3 = 100$ _____

2.3 Solving Equations by Adding

In this section we will <u>add</u> a number to both sides of an equation to solve the equation. Remember, the purpose of any technique is to get the variable by itself. Study this example:

$$x - 13 = 6$$

If we add 13 to both sides of this equation, we will get x by itself:

$$
\begin{array}{rcr}
x - 13 = & & 6 \\
+\,13 & & +\,13 \\
\hline
x \quad\;\; = & & 19
\end{array}
$$

- -

Here is another example:

$$y - 43 = 8$$

Adding 43 to both sides, we get:

$$
\begin{array}{rcr}
y - 43 = & & 8 \\
+\,43 & & +\,43 \\
\hline
y \quad\;\; = & & 51
\end{array}
$$

In these exercises, use this method of adding the same number to both sides of an equation to solve the equations.

✎ Exercises

Solve each equation.

1. $x - 13 = 17$ _____

2. $b - 300 = 500$ _____

3. $q - 54 = 102$ _____

4. $t - 4 = 0$ _____

5. $x - 70 = 120$ _____

6. $d - 61 = 82$ _____

7. $h - \dfrac{1}{2} = 4$ _____

8. $y - 125 = 600$ _____

9. $0 = z - 7.5$ _____

10. $5 = v - 5$ _____

2.4 *Solving Equations by Dividing*

Besides using addition and subtraction to solve equations, you can also use division. This example will show you how division is used:

$$6x = 24$$

If we divide both sides by 6:

$$\frac{6x}{6} = \frac{24}{6}$$
$$x = 4$$

Remember, the reason for dividing both sides of this equation by 6 is to get x by itself. The solution to $6x = 24$ is 4.

- -

Look at this example:

$$9y = 27$$

To get y by itself, we divide both sides by 9:

$$\frac{9y}{9} = \frac{27}{9}$$
$$y = 3$$

The solution to $9y = 27$ is 3.

To solve an equation, decide which operation will get the variable by itself.

✎ *Exercises*

Solve these equations.

1. $4x = 12$ _____

2. $5z = 20$ _____

3. $7q = 49$ _____

4. $32 = 8r$ _____

5. $17 + k = 80$ _____

6. $10x = 10$ _____

7. $n - 25 = 75$ _____

8. $56 = 8t$ _____

9. $3t = 4$ _____

10. $125 = x + 35$ _____

2.5 Solving Equations by Multiplying

Here is a review of the procedures you have learned so far to get the variable by itself.

1. When the variable is part of addition, such as:

$$x + 16 = 48$$

subtract.

2. If the variable is part of subtraction, such as:

$$y - 38 = 76$$

add.

3. When the variable is part of multiplication, as in this example:

$$7z = 63$$

divide.

In other words, **to solve an equation use the opposite operation**.

Therefore, if the variable is part of division, multiply.

- -

Here is an example showing the variable as part of division:

$$\frac{r}{3} = 5$$

We get r by itself by multiplying both sides by 3:

$$\frac{r}{3} \cdot 3 = 5 \cdot 3$$
$$r = 15$$

The solution to the equation $\frac{r}{3} = 5$ is 15.

- -

Here is another example of the variable as part of division:

$$\frac{s}{6} = 8$$

Since the variable is part of division, multiply both sides of the equation by 6:

$$\frac{s}{6} \cdot 6 = 8 \cdot 6$$
$$s = 48$$

The solution is 48.

- -

The procedures outlined above are summarized in this table.

Procedures for Solving Equations	
If the variable is part of . . .	**Use this operation . . .**
. . . addition . . . subtraction . . . multiplication . . . division	. . . subtraction . . . addition . . . division . . . multiplication

The procedure outlined here will help solve many equations.

Remember:

If the variable is part of an operation, then use the <u>opposite</u> operation to get the variable by itself.

Note: a fractional variable can be written in either of two ways:

$$\frac{2x}{3} \text{ can be written as } \frac{2}{3}x$$

$$\text{an expression like } \frac{4y}{7} + \frac{m}{2} \text{ can be written as } \frac{4}{7}y + \frac{1}{2}m$$

In most cases, we use the first way in this book. But you should be familiar with both.

✎ Exercises

Solve these equations.

1. $\frac{m}{7} = 5$ _____

2. $\frac{q}{12} = 1$ _____

3. $14 = \frac{r}{2}$ _____

4. $9c = 81$ _____

5. $17 + k = 82$ _____

6. $\frac{z}{8} = \frac{3}{8}$ _____

7. $\frac{m}{12} = \frac{1}{4}$ _____

8. $s - 48 = 12$ _____

9. $\frac{5}{8} = \frac{q}{16}$ _____

10. $\frac{a}{100} = 0$ _____

2.6 Solving Equations—Two Steps

You have been solving equations using one operation and only one step. Now you will solve equations using two steps. The job, again, will be to figure out how to get the variable by itself. Look at this example:

$$3x + 5 = 11$$

Step 1: Subtract 5 from both sides of the equation:

$$
\begin{aligned}
3x + 5 &= 11 \\
-5 & \quad -5 \\
\hline
3x &= 6
\end{aligned}
$$

Step 2: Divide both sides by 3:

$$\frac{3x}{3} = \frac{6}{3}$$
$$x = 2$$

The solution is 2.

- -

Here is another example. Study it carefully.

$$\frac{y}{3} - 2 = 5$$

Step 1: Add 2 to both sides of the equation:

$$\frac{y}{3} - 2 + \mathbf{2} = 5 + \mathbf{2}$$
$$\frac{y}{3} = 7$$

Step 2: Multiply both sides by 3:

$$\frac{y}{3} = 7$$
$$\frac{y}{3} \cdot \mathbf{3} = 7 \cdot \mathbf{3}$$
$$y = 21$$

The solution to the equation $\frac{y}{3} - 2 = 5$ is 21.

✎ Exercises

Solve these equations.

1. $2z - 5 = 7$ _____

2. $3r + 8 = 17$ _____

3. $18 = 4t - 2$ _____

4. $\frac{n}{6} - 4 = 8$ _____

5. $4x + 12 = 48$ _____

6. $\frac{y}{4} - 8 = 0$ _____

7. $2p - 6 = 24$ _____

8. $14m + 37 = 51$ _____

9. $30 = 4s + 2$ _____

10. $7 + \frac{t}{5} = 7$ _____

2.7 Solving Equations—Collec[t] Like Terms

If like terms (see Section 1.8) appear in an equation, collect them and solve th[e]

Study this example:

$$3x + 4x - 5x = 28$$

Step 1: Collect like terms:

$$3x + 4x - 5x = 28$$
$$2x = 28$$

Step 2: Divide both sides by 2:

$$\frac{2x}{2} = \frac{28}{2}$$
$$x = 14$$

The solution is 14.

- -

Sometimes you have to collect like terms from both sides of the equation:

$$6y = 12 + 4y$$

Step 1: Subtract 4y from both sides:

$$6y - \mathbf{4y} = 12 + 4y - \mathbf{4y}$$
$$2y = 12$$

Step 2: Divide both sides by 2:

$$\frac{2y}{2} = \frac{12}{2}$$
$$y = 6$$

The solution to $6y = 12 + 4y$ is 6.

✎ Exercises

Solve these equations:

1. $3z + 2z = 30$ _____

2. $14a - a = 26$ _____

3. $10b + 7b - 8b = 27$ _____

4. $t + t + t = 6$ _____

5. $34v + 20v - 18v = 0$ _____

6. $34 = 8m + 9m$ _____

7. $7x = 9 + 4x$ _____

8. $10y = 13 - 3y$ _____

9. $\frac{1}{3}m + \frac{2}{3}m = 16 - m$ (Remember— $\frac{1}{3}m$ is the same as $\frac{m}{3}$. And $\frac{2}{3}m$ is $\frac{2m}{3}$.) _____

10. $5r = 2r - r + 20$ _____

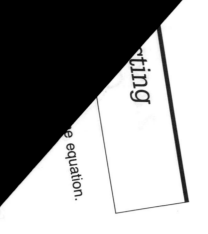

cient of the variable is a fraction:

$$\frac{3x}{4} = 9$$

$\frac{4}{3}$, the coefficient inverted:

$$\frac{}{4} \cdot \frac{4}{3} = 9 \cdot \frac{4}{3}$$

a fraction is multiplied by the fraction inverted, the product is 1. So the left-hand side of this equation is

$$1 \cdot x \text{ or } x$$

When we multiply on the right-hand side, we get:

$$x = \frac{9}{1} \cdot \frac{4}{3}$$
$$x = \frac{36}{3}$$
$$x = 12$$

The solution is 12.

— —

Here is another example:

$$\frac{2y}{3} = 16$$

We solve it in the same way as the preceding example. Multiply both sides by the coefficient inverted ($\frac{3}{2}$):

$$\frac{2}{3}y \cdot \frac{3}{2} = 16 \cdot \frac{3}{2}$$
$$1 \cdot y = \frac{16}{1} \cdot \frac{3}{2}$$
$$y = \frac{48}{2}$$
$$y = 24$$

The solution is 24.

Remember, the basic technique here is to ***multiply a fractional coefficient by the coefficient inverted***. It is important to do this work extra carefully, since there are many traps waiting.

— —

EXAMPLES

1. Here are three fractions and the same three fractions inverted:

Fraction	Inverted Fraction
$\dfrac{4}{5}$	$\dfrac{5}{4}$
$\dfrac{4}{7}$	$\dfrac{7}{4}$
$\dfrac{3}{4}$	$\dfrac{4}{3}$

2. To find the solution of

$$\frac{4z}{7} = 24 \text{ (Remember, this is the same as } \frac{4}{7}z = 24.)$$

multiply both sides by the coefficient inverted:

$$\frac{4}{7}z \cdot \frac{7}{4} = \frac{24}{1} \cdot \frac{7}{4}$$
$$z = \frac{168}{4}$$
$$z = 42$$

The solution to the equation is 42.

Do you see that we multiplied both sides of the equation by the coefficient inverted? We did this to get the variable z by itself.

✎ Exercises

Solve these equations.

1. $\dfrac{1}{2}s = 10$ _____

2. $\dfrac{5z}{6} = 25$ _____

3. $27 = \dfrac{3}{5}k$ _____

4. $\dfrac{2q}{3} + 3 = 21$ _____

5. $23 = \dfrac{4m}{5} - 1$ _____

6. $\dfrac{3}{8}r = 33$ _____

7. $\dfrac{4}{9}t = 64$ _____

8. $\dfrac{b}{7} = 1$ _____

9. $\dfrac{8}{9}a = 0$ _____

10. $22 = \dfrac{3x}{4} - 2$ _____

Which of these is an equation? Place a check mark ✔ next to the equations.

1. $4x^3 + 6 = 999$ _____

2. $13z - 8 < 42$ _____

3. $42t = 0$ _____

4. $7y > 14$ _____

5. $2a + 3b = 4c$ _____

6. $100t - s$ _____

7. $p^4 \cdot q \cdot r = 1$ _____

8. $12p - q + r^2 = q$ _____

Solve these equations.

9. $x + 9 = 27$ _____

10. $t - 14 = 23$ _____

11. $\dfrac{s}{3} = 13$ _____

12. $8q = 72$ _____

13. $\dfrac{m}{4} = 12$ _____

14. $2x - 7 = 13$ _____

15. $\dfrac{y}{2} - 8 = 10$ _____

16. $18a - 4a = 42$ _____

17. $\dfrac{3}{4}w = 12$ _____

18. $5z = 75$ _____

19. $\dfrac{5a}{3} = 10$ _____

20. $\dfrac{7m}{8} = 21$ _____

3. *Signed Numbers*

3.1 Understanding Signed Numbers

Algebraic expressions often make use of *signed numbers*.

You have probably used signed numbers many times, although you may not have called them by that name. For instance, if the temperature were to go 15 degrees below 0, you could use the minus sign to write the temperature as -15. A temperature above 0 could be marked with a plus sign, such as $+43$ for 43 degrees above zero.

Here is another example. Suppose your school were playing football, and just lost 8 yards on a play. You could write that as -8. A gain of 14 yards can be written as $+14$.

A business loss of $2000 could be written as -2000. You could write a gain of $7000 as $+7000$.

Numbers such as -15, $+43$, -8, $+14$, -2000, and $+7000$ are called "signed numbers." We call them "signed numbers" because they all use either a plus or minus sign.

We call -15 "negative 15" and $+43$ "positive 43."

When we write positive numbers, we usually do not use the plus sign. So 18 is the same as $+18$.

The only number without a sign is 0.

✎ *Exercises*

Write a number for each of these.

1. positive 35 _____

2. negative 3 _____

3. negative 150 _____

4. negative 0.3 _____

5. positive $\frac{1}{5}$ _____

6. positive 1400 _____

How do you read each of these numbers aloud?

7. $+8$ _____

8. -100 _____

9. 35 _____

10. -2.6 _____

11. -0.7 _____

12. $+\frac{1}{3}$ _____

13. Which number is the only number that is not a signed number? _____

14. Your school gained 47 yards on third down. How could you write that as a signed number? _____

15. If your business lost $2,000,000 last year, how could you write that as a signed number? _____

16. When the temperature is 23 below, what is this temperature as a signed number?

_____

3.2 Ordering Signed Numbers

A good way to understand signed numbers is to use a number line:

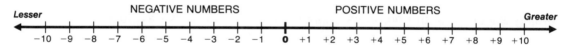

On this line, all numbers to the left of 0 are less than 0. They are written with a − sign, and are called **negative numbers**.

Numbers to the right of 0 are greater than 0. They are written with a + sign, and are called **positive numbers**. (Remember, we usually do not write the plus sign with positive numbers, but for the rest of this chapter we will use it for emphasis.)

Any number to the right of another number is the larger one. For instance, +6 is greater than +4; +2 is greater than −1; and −3 is greater than −4. Look at all of them on the number line.

- -

When we compare numbers we use the symbol < to mean **less than**. The smaller, pointed side of this symbol is next to the smaller number. Here are some examples:

$$+6 < +8 \text{ means } +6 \text{ is less than } +8$$
$$0 < +3 \text{ means } 0 \text{ is less than } +3$$
$$-5 < 0 \quad \text{means } -5 \text{ is less than } 0$$
$$-6 < +3 \text{ means } -6 \text{ is less than } +3$$

The symbol > means **greater than**. The larger, open side of the symbol is next to the larger number:

$$+9 > +2 \text{ means } +9 \text{ is greater than } +2$$
$$+2 > 0 \quad \text{means } +2 \text{ is greater than } 0$$
$$+5 > -5 \text{ means } +5 \text{ is greater than } -5$$
$$0 > -3 \text{ means } 0 \text{ is greater than } -3$$

- -

Be careful when you compare two negative numbers such as −10 and −8. Locate the numbers on the number line:

As you can see, −8 is to the right of −10. So we write

$$-8 > -10 \ (-8 \text{ is greater than } -10) \text{ or}$$
$$-10 < -8 \ (-10 \text{ is less than } -8)$$

As you can see, −8 is greater than −10, although +10 is greater than +8. Whenever you have to compare two negative numbers, you may want to draw a number line to make sure you have the correct comparison.

- -

In any comparison such as

$$-10 < +15$$

we can write the comparison another way:

$$+15 > -10$$

Reversing the order of the numbers changes the direction of the symbol.

✎ Exercises

Look at the number line. According to the number line, which number is greater?

1. +4 or −4 _____
2. 0 or −6 _____
3. 0 or +1 _____
4. $+\frac{1}{2}$ or +4 (Hint: on the number line, $+\frac{1}{2}$ is a point halfway between 0 and +1) _____

5. −13 or −12 _____
6. −8 or −1 _____
7. +7 or −7 _____
8. +2 or 0 _____

Write an **N** next to the negative numbers. Write a **P** next to the positive numbers.

9. −3 _____
10. −0.7 _____
11. +18 _____
12. +100 _____

13. 0 _____
14. $+\frac{1}{2}$ _____
15. −14 _____
16. +1 _____

After each of the following expressions write another comparison using the same numbers. (Remember, < means "less than"; > means "greater than.") The first one is done for you as an example.

17. +6 < +13 _+13 > +6_
18. −16 < 0 _____

19. −5 > −8 _____
20. +7 > −7 _____

Answer True (**T**) or False (**F**). Look at the number line if you're not sure.

21. −6 < 0 _____
22. +7 < 0 _____
23. −3 > +3 _____
24. −5 < −12 _____

25. −4 < −5 _____
26. −10 > +2 _____
27. 0 > −25 _____
28. −15 > −17 _____

3.3 Adding Positive Numbers

Positive numbers are numbers greater than 0. For emphasis in these next sections, we will use plus signs (+) for positive numbers.

You can show the sum of positive numbers on a number line. Here is an example:

$$(+3) + (+7) = +10$$

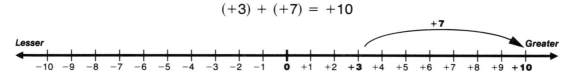

On the number line, when you add a _positive_ number, you move to the _right_.

Start with +3. Then jump 7 units to the right to +10. The sum is +10.

We add two positive numbers in the same way that we add numbers in arithmetic. When we add two positive numbers, the sum is also a positive number.

EXAMPLES

    1. $(+9) + (+20) = +29$

    2. $(+438) + 0 = +438$

    3. $(+3) + ? = +10$ means "find a number that replaces the ?." The answer is +7 because $(+3) + (+7) = +10$.

✎ Exercises

Write your answers as signed numbers.

    1. $(+6) + (+8) = ?$ _____

    2. $(+9) + 0 = ?$ _____

    3. $? + (+8) = +15$ _____

    4. $(+3) + (+8) + (+7) = ?$ _____

    5. $(+9) + ? = +9$ _____

    6. $(+50) + (+60) = ?$ _____

3.4 Adding Negative Numbers

Again we use the number line to see how two negative numbers can be added:

$$(-3) + (-4) = -7$$

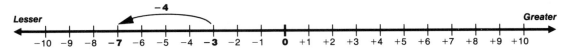

Start from −3. Then move 4 units to the left. The sum is −7.

- -

When you add two negative numbers, you add just as you do in arithmetic, except the answer is a negative number. The sum of two negative numbers is negative:

$$\begin{array}{r} -3 \\ + (-4) \\ \hline -7 \end{array}$$

EXAMPLES

1. $(-10) + (-12) = -22$

2. $(-15) + (-15) = -30$

3. $(-22) + 0 = -22$

4. $(-4) + ? = -10$ means "find the number that replaces the ? sign." The answer is −6, because $(-4) + (-6) = -10$.

✎ Exercises

1. $(-5) + (-8) = ?$ _____

2. $(-6) + ? = -9$ _____

3. $0 + (-7) = ?$ _____

4. $? + (-12) = -17$ _____

5. $(-8) + (-1) + (-5) = ?$ _____

6. $(-6) + (-8) + (-10) = ?$ _____

3.5 *Adding Positive and Negative Numbers*

How do we add a positive and a negative number? To help understand, let's study this example:

$$(+6) + (-3) = ?$$

Remember what you have learned about adding numbers on the number line: **move to the right for positive numbers; move to the left for negative numbers.**

Since the first number is +6, start at +6. And since the number you are adding is **negative** (-3), move 3 units to the **left**. Your answer is +3.

$$(+6) + (-3) = 3$$

- -

Here is another example to examine:

$$(-7) + (+5) = ?$$

Using the number line again, we have:

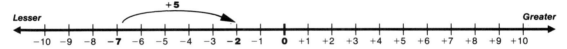

We start at -7. Then, since we are adding a **positive** number, we move 5 units to the **right**, to -2:

$$(-7) + (+5) = -2$$

- -

Here's how to add a positive and a negative number as an addition problem, without using the number line. We use a three-step procedure. Let's start with the first example above:

$$(+6) + (-3) = ?$$

Step 1. Change both numbers to unsigned numbers:

> +6 becomes 6
> −3 becomes 3

Step 2. Subtract the smaller number from the larger number:

$$6 - 3 = 3$$

Step 3. Write the sum, using the result of Step 2 and the original sign of the larger number. In this case, the original sign of the larger number(6) is +.

The sum is +3.

Here is the full equation: $\qquad (+6) + (-3) = +3$

Always follow this three-step procedure when adding a positive and a negative number.

- -

EXAMPLES

Follow the steps above to see how we get the results for each step.

1. $(-9) + (+5) = ?$

Step 1. -9 becomes 9 and $+5$ becomes 5.

Step 2. $9 - 5 = 4$

Step 3. The original sign of the larger number (9) is $-$. The sum is -4, and the full equation is:

$$(-9) + (+5) = -4$$

2. $(+12) + (-7) = ?$

Step 1. $+12$ becomes 12 and -7 becomes 7.

Step 2. $12 - 7 = 5$

Step 3. The original sign of the larger number (12) is $+$. The sum is $+5$, and the full equation is:

$$(+12) + (-7) = +5$$

✎ *Exercises*

Write your answers as signed numbers.

1. $(-12) + (+6) = $ _____

2. $(-15) + (+15) = $ _____

3. $(+8) + (-2) = $ _____

4. $(+11) + (-9) = $ _____

5. $(+6) + (-10) = $ _____

6. $(-2) + (+7) = $ _____

7. $(+14) + (-3) = $ _____

8. $(-1) + (+4) = $ _____

3.6 Subtracting a Positive Number From a Positive Number

In the last several lessons, you learned how to add signed numbers. The next few lessons will show you how to subtract them.

Let's start with a problem involving positive numbers and work it out on the number line:

$$(+9) - (+3) = +6$$

Begin at +9, then jump 3 units to the left. On a number line, when you subtract a positive number, you move to the left.

The answer to a subtraction problem is called the **difference**. In this problem, the difference is +6.

- -

Here is another example using the number line: $(+4) - (+12) = -8$

Start +4, then move 12 units to the left. You end up on −8. The difference is −8.

- -

If we weren't using plus signs to show positive numbers, then the last example would look like this:

$$4 - 12 = -8$$

Most of the time we don't use plus signs to show positive numbers.

EXAMPLES

1. $(+10) - (+3) = +7$

2. $(+347) - (+348) = -1$

3. $(+42) - (0) = +42$

✎ Exercises

Write your answers as signed numbers.

1. $(+2) - (+3) =$ _____

2. $(+9) - (+6) =$ _____

3. $(+849) - (+850) =$ _____

4. $(+7) - (+12) =$ _____

5. $(+8) - (+11) =$ _____

6. $(+95) - 0 =$ _____

3.7 Subtracting Other Signed Numbers

In section 3.6 you saw how to subtract a positive number from a positive number. In this section you will learn a single procedure that can be used to subtract in these other three cases:

Case 1. Subtracting a negative number from a negative number: $(-6) - (-3) = ?$

Case 2. Subtracting a negative number from a positive number: $(+6) - (-3) = ?$

Case 3. Subtracting a positive number from a negative number: $(-6) - (+3) = ?$

To illustrate, we show the procedure for Case 1—subtracting a negative number from a negative number. The procedure is the same for all three cases. It takes three steps.

$$\text{Example: } (-6) - (-3) = ?$$

Step 1. Change the sign of the second number:

$$-3 \text{ becomes } +3$$

Step 2. Add instead of subtract:

$$(-6) + (+3) = ?$$

Step 3. Use the technique of section 3.5—Adding positive and negative numbers—to find the answer to the equation:

$$(-6) + (+3) = -3$$

The answer (called the "difference") is -3 and the full original equation is

$$(-6) - (-3) = -3$$

This three-step procedure can be applied to all three subtraction cases above. (It also works when you're subtracting positive numbers, as in the last section.) The last two cases are illustrated in the examples below.

- -

EXAMPLES

Follow the three steps above to find the difference to these subtraction examples.

1. $(+6) - (-3) = ?$

Step 1. -3 becomes $+3$
Step 2. Add instead of subtract: $(+6) + (+3) = ?$
Step 3. $(+6) + (+3) = +9$

The difference is $+9$, and the full original equation is $(+6) - (-3) = +9$.

2. $(-6) - (+3) = ?$

Step 1. $+3$ becomes -3
Step 2. Add instead of subtract: $(-6) + (-3) = ?$
Step 3. $(-6) + (-3) = -9$

The difference is -9, and the full original equation is $(-6) - (+3) = -9$.

✎ Exercises

Use the three-step approach above to find the answers to these exercises. Remember to write your answers as signed numbers.

1. $(-7) - (-2) =$ _____

2. $(-15) - (+15) =$ _____

3. $(+4) - (-9) =$ _____

4. $(-10) - (-20) =$ _____

5. $(+10) - (-11) =$ _____

6. $(-100) - (-102) =$ _____

7. $(-5) - (+8) =$ _____

8. $(-300) - (+200) =$ _____

3.8 Multiplying Signed Numbers

To multiply two signed numbers, there are two rules:

Rule 1: *If the two numbers have the same sign (called <u>like</u> <u>signs</u>), then the product is <u>positive</u>.*

Rule 2: *If the two numbers have different signs (called <u>unlike</u> <u>signs</u>), then the product is <u>negative</u>.*

EXAMPLES

1. $(+4)\,(+7) = ?$ **Rule 1**—like signs: $(+4)\,(+7) = +28$

2. $(+5)\,(-8) = ?$ **Rule 2.**—unlike signs: $(+5)\,(-8) = -40$

3. $(-3)\,(-6) = ?$ **Rule 1.**—like signs: $(-3)\,(-6) = +18$

4. $(-1)\,(+9) = ?$ **Rule 2.**—unlike signs: $(-1)\,(+9) = -9$

Follow the two rules whenever you have to multiply signed numbers.

✎ Exercises

Remember to write all your answers as signed numbers.

1. $(-5)\,(-3) = $ _____

2. $(-3)\,(+7) = $ _____

3. $(+8)\,(-9) = $ _____

4. $(-1)\,(-115) = $ _____

5. $(+9)\,(+4) = $ _____

6. $(+6)\,(-2) = $ _____

7. $(-10)\,(-7) = $ _____

8. $(+5)\,(-8) = $ _____

3.9 *Dividing Signed Numbers*

The rules for dividing two signed numbers are the same as those for multiplying two signed numbers (see Section 3.8). Here are the two rules for dividing two signed numbers:

Rule 1: | *If the two numbers have the same sign (called **like** signs), then the quotient is **positive**.*

Rule 2: | *If the two numbers have different signs (called **unlike** signs), then the quotient is **negative**.*

These examples demonstrate how to apply these two rules.

EXAMPLES

1. $\dfrac{+12}{+3} = ?$ **Rule 1**—like signs: $\dfrac{+12}{+3} = +4$

2. $\dfrac{+15}{-5} = ?$ **Rule 2**—unlike signs: $\dfrac{+15}{-5} = -3$

3. $\dfrac{-20}{-4} = ?$ **Rule 1**—like signs: $\dfrac{-20}{-4} = +5$

4. $\dfrac{-14}{+2} = ?$ **Rule 2**—unlike signs: $\dfrac{-14}{+2} = -7$

✎ *Exercises*

Remember to write all your answers as signed numbers.

1. $\dfrac{+24}{-6} =$ _____

2. $\dfrac{-25}{-5} =$ _____

3. $\dfrac{+45}{-9} =$ _____

4. $\dfrac{-32}{-8} =$ _____

5. $\dfrac{-35}{-7} =$ _____

6. $\dfrac{+50}{+10} =$ _____

7. $\dfrac{-12}{+2} =$ _____

8. $\dfrac{+54}{-6} =$ _____

3.10 *Combining Like Terms*

The goal of combining like terms is to prepare an equation so that it can be solved. For instance, in this example

$$2x - 11x + 7x = 12$$

we shall combine like terms so that we can solve the equation.

Notice that there are three terms containing x:

$$2x, -11x, \text{ and } 7x$$

These are the like terms that will be combined. Two are positive like terms, one is a negative like term.

The combining of like terms and the solving of the equation is accomplished in these five steps:

Step 1. Add all positive like terms: $2x + 7x = 9x$

Step 2. Add all negative like terms: $-11x$

Step 3. Combine the results of Steps 1 and 2: $9x - 11x = -2x$

Step 4. Rewrite the original equation:

$$-2x = 12$$

Step 5. Divide both sides by -2:

$$\frac{-2x}{-2} = \frac{12}{-2}$$

$$x = -6$$

The solution is -6.

Study the combining of like terms in each of these examples below.

- -

EXAMPLES

1. $5z - 8z - 2z = 25$

Step 1. Add all positive like terms: $5z$

Step 2. Add all negative like terms: $-8z - 2z = -10z$

Step 3. Combine the results of Steps 1 and 2: $5z - 10z = -5z$

Step 4. Rewrite the original equation

$$-5z = 25$$

Step 5. Divide both sides by -5

$$\frac{-5z}{-5} = \frac{25}{-5}$$

$$z = -5$$

The solution is -5.

2. $-4t + 8t + 2t = 42$

Step 1. Add all positive like terms: $8t + 2t = 10t$

Step 2. Add all negative like terms: $-4t$

Step 3. Combine the results of Steps 1 and 2: $10t - 4t = 6t$

Step 4. Rewrite the original equation

$$6t = 42$$

Step 5. Divide both sides by 6

$$\frac{6t}{6} = \frac{42}{6}$$

$$t = 7$$

The solution is 7.

Use these five steps to help you combine like terms and solve equations.

✎ *Exercises*

Follow the steps above to solve these equations.

1. $7t - 4t = 24$ _____

2. $6y - 8y - y = 27$ _____

3. $-3s + 8s - 10s = 35$ _____

4. $18a - 14a = 36$ _____

5. $-5x + 7x - 10x = 48$ _____

6. $10z + 2z - 13z = 45$ _____

7. $-12r + 15r = 21$ _____

8. $-3b - 5b - 2b = 80$ _____

3.11 Chapter 3 Review

Which of these numbers are positive? Write a **P** next to the positive numbers.

1. $+8$ _____

2. -5 _____

3. 0 _____

4. 54 _____

5. $-\dfrac{1}{2}$ _____

Answer True or False. Write **T** next to the true statements and **F** next to the false statements.

6. $-4 > -5$ _____

7. $+13 > +12$ _____

8. $0 < -7$ _____

9. $-100 < -99$ _____

10. $-6 < 0$ _____

When you write the answers to the following, remember to write each one as a signed number.

Add.

11. $(-3) + (-5) =$ _____

12. $(-6) + (+4) =$ _____

13. $(+12) + (-14) =$ _____

14. $(+9) + (+4) =$ _____

15. $(+19) + (-20) =$ _____

16. $(-1) + (+101) =$ _____

Subtract.

17. $(+3) - (+2) =$ _____

18. $(-2) - (-3) =$ _____

19. $(-7) - (+6) =$ _____

20. $(+5) - (-8) =$ _____

21. $(-10) - (+12) =$ _____

22. $(-8) - (-2) =$ _____

Multiply or divide.

23. $(+4)\,(+3) =$ _____

24. $\dfrac{-45}{-9} =$ _____

25. $(-5)\,(+7) =$ _____

26. $\dfrac{-40}{-8} =$ _____

27. $\dfrac{+12}{-3} =$ _____

28. $(-2)\,(-8) =$ _____

29. $\dfrac{-24}{+3} =$ _____

30. $(-9)\,(-3) =$ _____

Solve.

31. $2x - 3x + 6x = 35$ _____

32. $4r - 8r - 2r = 36$ _____

33. $-5s - 2s - s = -16$ _____

34. $-2y + 6y - 3y = 34$ _____

35. $13a - 6a - 7a - 2a = 10$ _____

4. *Operations with Polynomials*

4.1 Adding and Subtracting Monomials

The word "term" refers to products such as

$$2x$$

$$14y$$

$$312abc$$

$$9r^2st$$

Another word that we often use for one term is ***monomial*** (pronounced like mun-OH-mee-ul). The four examples above are all monomials, but an expression like the following is not:

$$2x + 5y^2 z$$

It is not a monomial because it is made up of two terms.

- -

There are two kinds of monomials—***like monomials*** (or "like terms") and ***unlike monomials*** (or "unlike terms"). The following are ***like*** monomials:

$$+2ab^2$$

$$-8ab^2$$

$$+7ab^2$$

$$-14ab^2$$

They are like monomials because they all have the same variables, a and b, and the same exponents. All the a's have the same exponent, 1, and all the b's all have the same exponent, 2.

These monomials, on the other hand, are ***unlike*** monomials:

$$-20a^3$$

$$+7x$$

$$-18z^2$$

$$+12z^3$$

They either have different variables or different exponents for the same variable. The variables are a, x, and z. The two monomials with z's have different exponents, 2 and 3.

- -

As you learned in Section 1.8, we can add and subtract like monomials, but we cannot add or subtract unlike monomials. We add and subtract signed like monomials in the same way that we add and subtract signed numbers. Review the rules of Chapter 3 for adding and subtracting signed numbers. Then look at these next examples, which demonstrate the procedures with signed monomials.

EXAMPLES

1. $2x - 5x = -3x$

2. $4y + 9y = 13y$

3. $-7z + 3z = -4z$

4. $-3a^2 b^2 c + 10a^2 b^2 c - 5a^2 b^2 c = 2a^2 b^2 c$

5. $13t - 7t = 6t$

6. $14q + 7q - 8q = 13q$

✎ *Exercises*

Add or subtract.

1. $20m - 13m = $ _____

2. $12k + 8k = $ _____

3. $-7s + 14s = $ _____

4. $-11xy - 9xy = $ _____

5. $-2ab^2 c + 3ab^2 c = $ _____

6. $-3r^3 s^2 - 7r^3 s^2 + 5r^3 s^2 = $ _____

7. $6z + 3z + 2z = $ _____

8. $-4bc - 3bc - 8bc + 2bc = $ _____

9. $32q - 3q - 20q + 8q = $ _____

4.2 Polynomials

A monomial means one term. In Section 4.1 you studied how to add and subtract monomials. In this section we define what a polynomial is, and in the next section you will learn how to add and subtract polynomials.

A **polynomial** (pronounced like POLL-ee-NO-mee-ul) is an expression that consists of more than one term. Here are three examples of polynomials:

$$4x + 3y - 12z$$

$$-19z^3 - 2z^2$$

$$42a - 13$$

A polynomial consisting of two terms is called a **binomial**.

A polynomial consisting of three terms is called a **trinomial**.

The polynomial $7a + 5b$ is a binomial.

The polynomial $-2x^2 + 3x - 5$ is a trinomial.

– –

When a polynomial has the same variable, it is often useful to put the polynomial in order. ***Putting a polynomial in order*** means placing the powers of the same variable in decreasing order. Here is an example:

$$5x^3 + 3x^2 - 7x - 2$$

Notice that the powers of $x\,(3,2,1)$ are in decreasing order and that they are followed by the number -2. If there is a number by itself, like the -2, then it is placed at the end.

Here is an example of a polynomial that is not in order:

$$-2y^2 + 17 - 35y + y^3$$

The polynomial is not in order because the powers of y—2,1,3—are not in decreasing order and the number 17 is not at the end. Rearranging the terms, we put the polynomial in order:

$$y^3 - 2y^2 - 35y + 17$$

– –

EXAMPLES

1. These are monomials:

$$2x$$
$$-5y^2$$
$$700r$$

2. These are binomials:

$$-16a + 25$$
$$4r^3 + 17s$$
$$13 - 27x$$

3. These are trinomials:

$$-2a + 3b - 7c$$
$$7x^2 + 38x - 3$$
$$22r + 23s - 6$$

4. These trinomials are <u>not</u> in order:

$$6a - 5 + 9a^2$$
$$2 - 7x + 7x^2$$
$$13 - t^2 + t$$

5. Here are the trinomials of Example 4 in order:

$$9a^2 + 6a - 5$$
$$7x^2 - 7x + 2$$
$$-t^2 + t + 13$$

6. Binomials and trinomials are polynomials, but monomials are not.

Identify each of these expressions as a monomial, a binomial, a trinomial, or a polynomial. Some of these expressions will have two words identifying them. (The first one is done for you as an example.)

1. $2x + 3y$ *binomial, polynomial*

2. $-6u^2 - 4u - 80$ _____

3. $35a$ _____

4. $19 - 200t$ _____

5. $5p^2 - 17q + 2r$ _____

6. -14 _____

7. $1 + 2x - 3x^2$ _____

8. $-2a - 3$ _____

9. $600t$ _____

10. $-2a^2 - 3a - 5$ _____

Put a check mark next to the following polynomials that are in order.

11. $2 + 3x + 3x^2$ _____

12. $-4 - 7t + 8t^3$ _____

13. $s - 5$ _____

14. $17 - r^2$ _____

15. $800 - y$ _____

16. $5m^2 - 2m + 19$ _____

17. $9r^3 - 1000$ _____

18. $-23d^3 + 9d^2 + 2d - 11$ _____

Rewrite these polynomials in order. (The first one has been done for you.)

19. $7 - 3x + 5x^2$ *5x² - 3x + 7*

20. $6t + 5t^2 - 13$ _____

21. $3 + 5r$ _____

22. $9 + 5s^2 - 15s$ _____

23. $-18 - 2a^3 - a^2$ _____

24. $12 + q^2$ _____

4.3 Adding and Subtracting Polynomials

The rule of Sections 4.1 and 1.8 state that we can add or subtract only like monomials. In this section we use this rule to add two polynomials:

To add or subtract two polynomials, combine the _like_ terms.

Let's look at some problems that illustrate this:

Problem 1:

Add: $2x + 3y$ and $5x + 6y$

The like terms are those with an x or those with a y. Combine the like terms by placing the like terms under each other. Then add column by column:

$$\begin{array}{r} 2x + 3y \\ \underline{5x + 6y} \\ 7x + 9y \end{array}$$

The sum is $7x + 9y$.

- -

Problem 2:

Add: $5a + 3b$ and $-12a - 7b$

Combine the like terms. Place the like terms under each other and add column by column:

$$\begin{array}{r} 5a + 3b \\ \underline{-12a - 7b} \\ -7a - 4b \end{array}$$

The sum is $-7a - 4b$.

This process of adding or combining like terms is the way we simplify polynomials. (The word *simplify* means to combine or add the like terms of a polynomial.)

- -

Problem 3:

To simplify the polynomial

$$14 - 9a + 6 + 11a$$

place the like terms in a column. Then add each column as we did in Problems 1 and 2:

$$\begin{array}{r} -9a + 14 \\ 11a + 6 \\ \hline 2a + 20 \end{array}$$

The polynomial is now simplified as $2a + 20$.

- -

Problem 4:

Here is another example of simplifying by adding or combining like terms:

$$18 - 2x^3 + 4x^2 + 5x - 10x^2 + 3x^3 - 12x - 12$$

Combine like terms by placing them in columns and adding:

$$\begin{array}{r} -2x^3 + 4x^2 + 5x + 18 \\ 3x^3 - 10x^2 - 12x - 12 \\ \hline x^3 - 6x^2 - 7x + 6 \end{array}$$

The polynomial is now simplified:

$$x^3 - 6x^2 - 7x + 6$$

✎ *Exercises*

Add these polynomials.

1. $7r + 3s + 10t$ and $-4r - t - 8t$

_____

2. $2y^3 + 3y^2$ and $-7y - 13y^3 - 9y^2$

_____

3. $-a^2 + 4b^2 + 8a^2$ and $-13a^2 + 5a^2$

$- 7b^2$ _____

4. $20 - 3x + 12$ and $-5x - 7x + 10$

_____

Simplify each polynomial.

5. $z^3 - 18 + 22 - z^3$ _____

6. $2x - 7y^2 - 12y^2 + 17y^2 - 8$

_____

7. $14 - 4b - 7b + 19b$ _____

8. $7w^3 + 3v^2 - 13 - 8v^2 - 9v^2 + 7$

_____

4.4 *Exponents in Multiplying Variables*

In the previous sections you learned how to add and subtract both monomials and polynomials. Now you are ready to start learning how to multiply monomials.

The technique for multiplying two monomials depends upon understanding how to multiply two variables. In Section 1.9 we looked briefly at this method. The present section reviews that earlier work, and introduces a new multiplication technique.

In the multiplication problem

$$(z^2)\,(z^4) = ?$$

z is the variable of both terms z^2 and z^4. The exponents are 2 and 4. The coefficient of both terms is 1. Here is what the exponents mean:

$$(z^2)\,(z^4) = (z \cdot z)\,(z \cdot z \cdot z \cdot z)$$
$$(z^2)\,(z^4) = z \cdot z \cdot z \cdot z \cdot z \cdot z$$
$$(z^2)\,(z^4) = z^6$$

The product of z^2 and z^4 is z^6. Now look at the problem, and notice that we can also **add the exponents** of the terms z^2 and z^4 to get the exponent of the product: $2 + 4 = 6$.

- -

Look at another problem:

$$(x^5)\,(x^3) = ?$$

In this problem we multiply two terms having x as the variable and both having the coefficient 1:

$$(x^5)\,(x^3) = (x \cdot x \cdot x \cdot x \cdot x)\,(x \cdot x \cdot x)$$
$$(x^5)\,(x^3) = x \cdot x \cdot x \cdot x \cdot x \cdot x \cdot x \cdot x$$
$$(x^5)\,(x^3) = x^8$$

The product of x^5 and x^3 is x^8. We add the exponents of the terms x^5 and x^3 to get the exponent of the product: $5 + 3 = 8$.

- -

Here's the rule:

> **To multiply two terms using the same variable, add the exponents.**

- -

EXAMPLES

We use the rule above for exponents to find the products.

1. $(s^2) (s^3) = s^5$

2. $(y^6) (y) = y^7$

3. $(z^5) (z^4) = z^9$

4. $(r) (r^2) (r^3) = (r) (r \cdot r) (r \cdot r \cdot r)$
$$= (r \cdot r \cdot r \cdot r \cdot r \cdot r)$$
$$= r^6$$

(Remember: r is equivalent to r^1. In adding exponents, we add $1 + 2 + 3 = 6$)

5. $(q^5) (q^3) (q^2) = q^{10}$

✎ *Exercises*

Use the rule for exponents to find these products.

1. $(w) (w^2) =$ _____

2. $(x^2) (x^3) =$ _____

3. $(m^6) (m) =$ _____

4. $(k^7) (k^3) =$ _____

5. $(s^6) (s) (s^4) =$ _____

6. $(y^2) (y^3) (y^4) =$ _____

7. $(z^6) (z^8) =$ _____

4.5 *Multiplying Monomials*

To multiply two monomials, we use the rule in Section 4.4 for multiplying two variables. This example will illustrate the technique:

$$(7x^2)\,(3x^3)$$

There are three steps to multiply these two monomials:

Step 1: Multiply the coefficients of each monomial first: $(7)\,(3) = 21$

Step 2: Multiply the variables: $(x^2)\,(x^3) = x^5$

Step 3: Multiply the results of the first two steps to get the answer: $(21)\,(x^5) = 21x^5$

- -

Here is another example using these three steps:

$$(5r^4)\,(-7r^5) = ?$$

Step 1: $(5)\,(-7) = -35$

Step 2: $(r^4)\,(r^5) = r^9$

Step 3: $(-35)\,(r^9) = -35r^9$

Use these three steps to multiply any two monomials.

EXAMPLES

1. $(6j^3)\,(2j) = 12j^4$

2. $(-3s^6)\,(4s^3) = -12s^9$

3. $(z^7)\,(5z^2) = 5z^9$

4. $(-2y^5)\,(-9y^2) = 18y^7$

5. $(7a^4)\,(-a) = -7a^5$

6. $(-x^4)\,(x^2) = -x^6$

✎ *Exercises*

1. $(2a^4)\,(8a^2) =$ _____

2. $(-3x^3)\,(7x^5) =$ _____

3. $(y)\,(y^4) =$ _____

4. $(-9v^3)\,(-9v^3) =$ _____

5. $(4z^7)\,(-5z^8) =$ _____

6. $(8q^9)\,(9q^2) =$ _____

7. $(-s^3)\,(-4s^2) =$ _____

8. $(w)\,(w) =$ _____

9. $(b^4)\,(-2b^3) =$ _____

10. $(-4p^5)\,(-10p^4) =$ _____

4.6 Exponents in Dividing Variables

To multiply variables, we have an addition rule for exponents (see Section 4.4). Is there a similar rule for dividing variables?

Let's start by looking at a division example:

$$\frac{x^4}{x^2}$$

In this example, the coefficient of x^4 and x^2 is 1, and the exponents are 4 and 2. This is what the exponents mean:

$$\frac{x \cdot x \cdot x \cdot x}{x \cdot x}$$

Cancelling two x's from the numerator and denominator, we have:

$$\frac{\cancel{x} \cdot \cancel{x} \cdot x \cdot x}{\cancel{x} \cdot \cancel{x}}$$

$$x \cdot x \text{ or } x^2$$

The quotient is x^2. Observe that we can also arrive at the exponent of the answer by subtracting exponents: $4 - 2 = 2$.

- -

Another example will demonstrate the same idea:

$$\frac{s^6}{s^3}$$

Writing out these exponents, we have:

$$\frac{s \cdot s \cdot s \cdot s \cdot s \cdot s}{s \cdot s \cdot s}$$

Next, we cancel three s's from the numerator and denominator to get:

$$\frac{\cancel{s} \cdot \cancel{s} \cdot \cancel{s} \cdot s \cdot s \cdot s}{\cancel{s} \cdot \cancel{s} \cdot \cancel{s}}$$

$$s \cdot s \cdot s \text{ or } s^3$$

The quotient is s^3. We could have obtained the same exponent by subtracting exponents: $6 - 3 = 3$.

- -

These two examples suggest the rule for dividing variables:

> *To divide two terms that contain the same variable, subtract the exponents.*

- -

EXAMPLES

In these examples we use the rule above for dividing variables.

1. $\dfrac{r^3}{r^2} = r$ $(3 - 2 = 1)$

2. $\dfrac{x^7}{x^4} = x^3$ $(7 - 4 = 3)$

3. $\dfrac{t^5}{t^2} = t^3$ $(5 - 2 = 3)$

4. $\dfrac{z^3}{z} = z^2$ $(3 - 1 = 2)$

5. $\dfrac{w^{10}}{w^5} = w^5$ $(10 - 5 = 5)$

✎ Exercises

Use the rule above for dividing variables.

1. $\dfrac{q^4}{q^2} =$ _____

2. $\dfrac{y^7}{y^3} =$ _____

3. $\dfrac{m^6}{m} =$ _____

4. $\dfrac{x^9}{x^8} =$ _____

5. $\dfrac{z^3}{z^2} =$ _____

6. $\dfrac{n^{10}}{n^2} =$ _____

7. $\dfrac{p^5}{p} =$ _____

8. $\dfrac{a^{12}}{a^8} =$ _____

4.7 Dividing Monomials

To divide one monomial by another monomial, make use of the rule for dividing variables (see Section 4.6). Here is an example:

$$\frac{16x^4}{2x^2}$$

Divide $16x^4$ by $2x^2$ in three steps:

Step 1: Divide the coefficients: $\frac{16}{2} = 8$

Step 2: Divide the variables: $\frac{x^4}{x^2} = x^2$

Step 3: Multiply the results of Steps 1 and 2: $(8)\ (x^2) = 8x^2$

The quotient of $16x^4$ divided by $2x^2$ is $8x^2$.

- -

Dividing one monomial by another simplifies an expression. In the example above, we simplified $\frac{16x^4}{2x^2}$ to $8x^2$.

We apply the three steps above to simplify another expression:

$$\frac{-35t^5}{5t^3}$$

Step 1: $\frac{-35}{5} = -7$

Step 2: $\frac{t^5}{t^3} = t^2$

Step 3: $-7t^2$

The quotient is $-7t^2$. We have simplified $\frac{-35t^5}{5t^3}$ to $-7t^2$.

Remember these three steps whenever you want to divide a monomial by another monomial.

- -

The three steps apply only to two monomials that have the same variables. You **cannot** use all three steps with this example:

$$\frac{15a^3}{3b^2}$$

because a and b are different variables. Only Step 1 applies:

$$\frac{15a^3}{3b^2} = \frac{5a^3}{b^2}$$

The expression $\frac{15a^3}{3b^2}$ is simplified to $\frac{5a^3}{b^2}$.

EXAMPLES

1. $\dfrac{24s^4}{-6s^3} = -4s$

2. $\dfrac{33r^7}{11r^4} = 3r^3$

3. $\dfrac{18r^3}{9s^2} = \dfrac{2r^3}{s^2}$ is as far as we can simplify the expression because r and s are different variables.

4. $\dfrac{-72x^8}{-9x^5} = 8x^3$ Note that this simplification is positive!

5. $\dfrac{6y^4}{7z^2}$ This expression **cannot** be simplified any further because $\dfrac{6}{7}$ cannot be reduced and y and z are different variables.

6. $\dfrac{-3a^4}{8a^2} = \dfrac{-3a^2}{8}$ Note that $\dfrac{a^4}{a^2}$ reduces to a^2, but $\dfrac{-3}{8}$ cannot be reduced.

7. $\dfrac{9q^3}{10q^3} = \dfrac{9}{10}$ Here's why. First, $\dfrac{q^3}{q^3} = 1$ because it has the same numerator and denominator. We use this fact in these steps:

$$\begin{aligned}
\frac{9q^3}{10q^3} &= \left(\frac{9}{10}\right)\left(\frac{q^3}{q^3}\right) \\
&= \left(\frac{9}{10}\right)(1) \\
&= \frac{9}{10}
\end{aligned}$$

The variable q in the numerator and denominator has the same exponent. If that happens in an expression, then that part of the expression equals 1.

✎ Exercises

Which of these expressions **cannot** be simplified any further? Indicate by placing an **N** next to the expression. Leave the rest blank.

1. $\dfrac{r^4}{s^2}$ _____

2. $\dfrac{35a^5}{5a^3}$ _____

3. $\dfrac{-42x^8}{7y^7}$ _____

4. $\dfrac{13p^4}{5q^2}$ _____

5. $\dfrac{2w^8}{-3w^2}$ _____

6. $\dfrac{x^6}{y^5}$ _____

Use the 3-step procedure outlined above to simplify each of these expressions.

7. $\dfrac{-28x^3}{7x^2} =$ _____

8. $\dfrac{a^5}{a^4} =$ _____

9. $\dfrac{45r^3}{9r^2} =$ _____

10. $\dfrac{3w^8}{15w^7} =$ _____

11. $\dfrac{36d^7}{-6d^2} =$ _____

12. $\dfrac{54g^9}{9g^5} =$ _____

13. $\dfrac{-4r^3}{6r^2} =$ _____

14. $\dfrac{-18s^4}{-3s^4} =$ _____

4.8 Multiplying a Polynomial by a Monomial

Multiplying a polynomial by a monomial is really not very different from multiplying two monomials (Section 4.5). Simply follow two steps:

Step 1. Multiply each term of the polynomial by the monomial.

Step 2. Combine.

Here's an example:

$$6(a + b) = 6(a) + 6(b)$$
$$= 6a + 6b$$

- -

Here's a slightly more complex example. Notice the signs:

$$4x(3x - y) = 4x(3x) - 4x(y)$$
$$= 12x^2 - 4xy$$

- -

Finally, a slightly tricky one. Don't get thrown off by the signs! Remember, $-$ times $-$ is $+$. (See Example 3 in Section 3.8):

$$-2m(m^2 - 3n) = (-2m)(m^2) - (-2m)(3n)$$
$$= -2m^3 + 6mn$$

EXAMPLES

Here are five more examples for you to examine. They all illustrate the technique shown above.

1. $5(x - y) = 5(x) - 5(y) = 5x - 5y$

2. $7(2r + 3s) = 7(2r) + 7(3s)$
$$= 14r + 21s$$

3. $-3(4y - 8z) = (-3)(4y) - (-3)(8z)$
$$= -12y + 24z$$

4. $-2z(5 - 3z) = (-2z)(5) - (-2z)(3z)$
$$= -10z + 6z^2$$

5. $4x(9x^2 + y) = 4x(9x^2) + 4x(y)$
$$= 36x^3 + 4xy$$

Multiply. Put each answer in order (see Lesson 4.2).

1. $2(a - 5) =$ _____

2. $4(p + 2q) =$ _____

3. $j(7 - k) =$ _____

4. $-3(r + s) =$ _____

5. $-5y(2x - 5y) =$ _____

6. $12a(a^2 - 3b) =$ _____

7. $-7x(x^2 + 2x^3) =$ _____

8. $-25(4 - 3t) =$ _____

4.9 *Solving Equations Containing Parentheses*

In this section, we make use of the technique of the previous section to solve equations with parentheses. An example illustrates how this is done:

$$2(x - 5) + 6x = 14$$

The first step is to multiply the monomial times the polynomial:

$$2(x - 5) = 2(x) - 2(5)$$
$$= 2x - 10$$

Then apply the usual procedure for solving equations:

$$2(x - 5) + 6x = 14$$
$$2x - 10 + 6x = 14 \text{ (The result of the first step, above)}$$
$$8x - 10 = 14$$
$$8x - 10 + \mathbf{10} = 14 + \mathbf{10}$$
$$8x = 24$$
$$x = 3$$

The solution to the equation is 3.

- -

This next example is a little tougher:

$$12(a + 2) - 3 = -3(2 - a)$$

This example has two expressions where a monomial multiplies a polynomial, one on each side of the equation.

Multiplying first on the *left*-hand side of the equation:

$$12(a + 2) - 3 = -3(2 - a)$$
$$12(a) + 12(2) - 3 = -3(2 - a)$$
$$12a + 24 - 3 = -3(2 - a)$$
$$12a + 21 = -3(2 - a)$$

Watch the multiplying on the *right*-hand side of the equation. It is somewhat tricky, because the monomial is negative:

$$12a + 21 = -3(2 - a)$$
$$12a + 21 = (-3)(2) - (-3)a$$
$$12a + 21 = -6 + 3a$$

Solve this last equation in the usual way:

Subtract 3a from each side of the equation:	$12a + 21 - \mathbf{3a} = -6 + 3a - \mathbf{3a}$
Simplify:	$9a + 21 = -6$
Subtract 21 from each side:	$9a + 21 - \mathbf{21} = -6 - \mathbf{21}$
Simplify:	$9a = -27$
Divide both sides by 9:	$a = -3$

The solution to the equation is −3.

✎ Exercises

Solve.

1. $4(x + 1) = 12$ _____

2. $6(2z - 1) = 30$ _____

3. $-3s = -5(s - 8)$ _____

4. $8(5 - y) = 64$ _____

5. $-7(3r + 4) = 14$ _____

6. $4(c - 4) = 3(c + 5)$ _____

4.10 *Multiplying Binomials— Vertical Multiplication*

Now you are ready to learn how to multiply binomials. Here is an example:

$$(2x + 4)(3x + 5) = ?$$

To find the product, we first place the two binomials under each other as we would if we were multiplying two ordinary numbers. When we place the binomials under each other to multiply, we call this type of multiplication **vertical multiplication**:

$$\begin{array}{r} 2x + 4 \\ \underline{3x + 5} \end{array}$$

Vertical multiplication of binomials is just like ordinary multiplication, with two small differences:

1. You don't have to "carry." That makes things easier.
2. You do have to pay attention to signs.

- -

To multiply $(2x + 4)(3x + 5)$, we start off by multiplying the entire top line of the problem by the 5 in the bottom line (just like an ordinary multiplication problem):

$$\begin{array}{r} 2x + 4 \\ \underline{3x + 5} \\ 10x + 20 \end{array}$$

Next, we multiply the entire top line by the $3x$ in the bottom line—again, just like an ordinary multiplication problem:

$$\begin{array}{r} 2x + 4 \\ \underline{3x + 5} \\ 10x + 20 \\ 6x^2 + 12x \phantom{{}+ 20} \end{array}$$

Notice how the like terms line up, one under the other.

Now we complete the problem by adding, column by column:

$$\begin{array}{r} 2x + 4 \\ \underline{3x + 5} \\ 10x + 20 \\ \underline{6x^2 + 12x \phantom{{}+ 20}} \\ 6x^2 + 22x + 20 \end{array}$$

The product is $6x^2 + 22x + 20$.

- -

Here's another example of vertical multiplication. This example contains a negative number, so you have to be careful of the signs:

$$
\begin{array}{r}
3y - 8 \\
5y + 4 \\
\hline
12y - 32 \\
15y^2 - 40y \\
\hline
15y^2 - 28y - 32
\end{array}
$$

The product is $15y^2 - 28y - 32$. Look carefully at the problem and make sure you understand what the minus sign does to the multiplication and to the addition.

✎ Exercises

Use vertical multiplication to find these products.

1. $(x + 3)(x + 2) = $ _____

2. $(4t - 1)(3t + 1) = $ _____

3. $(3z - 2)(5z + 6) = $ _____

4. $(4r + 7)(7r + 4) = $ _____

5. $(3x - 2)(9x - 1) = $ _____

6. $(w - 8)(w + 8) = $ _____

7. $(2a + 6)(9a - 3) = $ _____

4.11 Multiplying Binomials—Horizontal Multiplication

In Section 4.10 we looked at the method of vertical multiplication for multiplying two binomials. In this section we learn another method—*horizontal multiplication*.

Let's see what this means by looking at an example:

$$(4x + 6)(3x + 7) = ?$$

In horizontal multiplication we do not line up the binomials under each other, but leave them in this horizontal position.

We do the multiplication in several steps:

Step 1. Multiply the *first* terms of the two binomials:

$$(\mathbf{4x} + 6)(\mathbf{3x} + 7) = \mathbf{12x^2} \ldots \ldots$$

Step 2. Multiply the *outside* terms:

$$(\mathbf{4x} + 6)(3x + \mathbf{7}) = 12x^2 + \mathbf{28x} \ldots$$

Step 3. Multiply the *inside* terms:

$$(4x + \mathbf{6})(\mathbf{3x} + 7) = 12x^2 + 28x + \mathbf{18x} \ldots$$

Step 4. Multiply the *last* terms:

$$(4x + \mathbf{6})(3x + \mathbf{7}) = 12x^2 + 28x + 18x + \mathbf{42}$$

Step 5. Combine the like terms (from Steps 2 and 3):

$$= 12x^2 + \mathbf{28x} + \mathbf{18x} + 42$$
$$= 12x^2 + \mathbf{46x} \qquad + 42$$

The product of the binomials $(4x + 6)(3x + 7)$ is $12x^2 + 46x + 42$.

- -

Look back at Steps 1-4. Notice that, altogether, there are four products:

First terms
Outside terms
Inside terms
Last terms

When doing horizontal multiplication, these are the four products that you add to get the product.

To remember the order of multiplication we combine the four first letters above—*F, O, I* and *L*—into the word *FOIL*.

FOIL tells you the order in which to multiply the terms of the binomials—*F* for first, *O* for outside, *I* for inside and *L* for last.

Here is the complete **FOIL** method for the example above:

$$\text{F} \quad\quad \text{O} \quad\quad \text{I} \quad\quad \text{L}$$
$$(4x + 6)(3x + 7) = 12x^2 + 28x + 18x + 42$$

Add the like terms:
$$28x + 18x = 46x$$

$$(4x + 6)(3x + 7) = 12x^2 + 46x + 42$$

EXAMPLES

We use **FOIL** to find the product of each of these binomials.

1. $(4x + 2)(8x + 1) = ?$

$$\textbf{F}: (4x)(8x) = 32x^2$$
$$\textbf{O}: (4x)(1) = 4x$$
$$\textbf{I}: (2)(8x) = 16x$$
$$\textbf{L}: (2)(1) = 2$$

Add the like terms to get $4x + 16x = 20x$

The product is

$$(4x + 2)(8x + 1) = 32x^2 + 20x + 2$$

2. $(4y + 5)(2y - 3) = ?$ (Be careful of the minus sign here!)

$$\textbf{F}: (4y)(2y) = 8y^2$$
$$\textbf{O}: (4y)(-3) = -12y$$
$$\textbf{I}: (5)(2y) = 10y$$
$$\textbf{L}: (5)(-3) = -15$$

Add **O** and **I** (the like terms) to get:

$$-12y + 10y = -2y$$

$$(4y + 5)(2y - 3) = 8y^2 - 2y - 15$$

$$\text{F} \quad\ \text{O} \quad \text{I} \quad\ \text{L}$$
3. $(3t + 8)(t - 2) = 3t^2 - 6t + 8t - 16$
$$= 3t^2 + 2t - 16$$

✎ *Exercises*

Find the products by horizontal multiplication. Use **FOIL**.

1. $(t + 7)(t + 3) =$ _____

2. $(s + 5)(4s + 9) =$ _____

3. $(3a - 6)(8a + 2) =$ _____

4. $(n - 9)(2n - 4) =$ _____

5. $(10x + 5)(3x + 2) =$ _____

6. $(y + 4)(y - 4) =$ _____

7. $(12z - 2)(z + 1) =$ _____

4.12 Chapter 4 Review

This test is a way for you to check up on your mastery of the skills of Chapter 4.

Mark each of these expressions as a monomial (**M**), a binomial (**B**), a trinomial (**T**) or a polynomial (**P**). Some expressions will be marked twice.

1. $17k$ _____

2. $23a + 37b$ _____

3. $-13y$ _____

4. $7z^2 + 4z - 8$ _____

5. -85 _____

6. $4 - 7s^2 + 16s$ _____

Simplify each polynomial.

7. $12 - 3a + 3 + 7a$ _____

8. $4x^2 - 2x^2 + 6 + 9x^2 - 6x^2 - 2$ ____

9. $c - 12 + 9c + 20$ _____

Multiply or divide.

10. $(3a^2)(2a^3) =$ _____

11. $(b^2)(-3b^4) =$ _____

12. $\dfrac{6z^4}{2z^3} =$ _____

13. $4(5 - r) =$ _____

14. $(-6x^5)(-4x^3) =$ _____

15. $-3y(2y - 5) =$ _____

Solve each equation.

16. $2(x + 1) = 12$ _____

17. $-3(8 - y) = 3$ _____

18. $5(2w - 1) = 15$ _____

19. $4(d - 1) = 3(d + 1)$ _____

Use the vertical multiplication method to find each product.

20. $(4x + 2)(5x + 7)$ _____

21. $(3x + 1)(2x - 5)$ _____

22. $(2a - 3)(3a - 2)$ _____

Use the horizontal multiplication method to find each product.

23. $(m + 4)(2m + 1)$ _____

24. $(3m + 2)(2m - 5)$ _____

25. $(4m - 3)(2m - 6)$ _____

5. *Inequalities*

5.1 What Is an Inequality?

When we write an equation, we use an equals sign (=). For equations such as:

$$38 + 6 = 44$$
$$(-4) + (-6) = -10$$
$$6x + 9 = 15$$

the equals sign means that the left-hand side is equal to the right-hand side.

In contrast to an equation, an **inequality** is a statement that the left-hand side is NOT equal to the right-hand side. Here is an example:

$$17 + 2 < 25$$

which we read as "17 plus 2 is <u>less than</u> 25."

Here are some symbols that inequalities use:

$\neq$ **not equal to**
$<$ **less than**
$>$ **greater than**
$\leqq$ **less than or equal to** (sometimes written like $\leq$)
$\geqq$ **greater than or equal to** (sometimes written like $\geq$)

When comparing two numbers, we can use a number line. It is frequently helpful in determining which number is smaller or bigger:

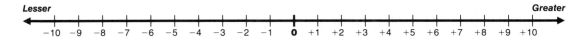

From this number line, we can tell that each of these is true:

$$0 < 6$$
$$-4 < 0$$
$$7 > -6$$
$$-4 > -8$$

- -

Note how the symbols $<$ and $>$ combine with the equals sign, making the following inequalities true.

$6 \leqq 10$ (It may seem strange to say that 6 is **less than or equal to** 10, but it's true.)

$6 \leqq 6$

$-3 \geqq -7$

$-3 \geqq -3$

- -

We can use variables as well as ordinary numbers in an equality. When we write $x \leqq 5$, we mean that x can stand for all numbers less than 5 or equal to 5.

We can represent $x \leqq 5$ on a number line by drawing a line above the number line ending in a black dot. We place the dot over 5 to show that 5 is also included, since x is less than **or equal to** 5.

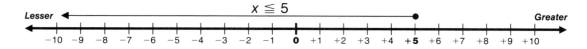

- -

In a similar manner, we represent $z > -2$ by drawing a line with a dot that is *not* blacked in. We place this "open dot" over -2 to show that -2 is **not** included, since z is **greater than** -2 but not equal to it.

You can use the number line to help you determine which number in an inequality is bigger or smaller.

✎ *Exercises*

Which of these is true? Mark a **T** next to the ones that are true and an **F** next to the ones that are false.

1. $2 < 22$ _____

2. $-3 > 3$ _____

3. $0 > -1$ _____

4. $6 \neq 7$ _____

5. $12 > 12$ _____

6. $-5 \leqq -5$ _____

7. $-15 = -15$ _____

8. $4 < 0$ _____

Represent each of these on a number line.

9. $a > 3$

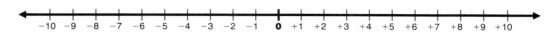

10. $b < -1$

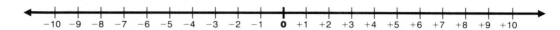

11. $c \geqq 0$

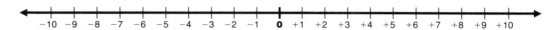

5.2 Rules for Inequalities

In this chapter we will learn how to solve inequalities, but first we have to learn several rules about inequalities.

Rule 1: | **You can add or subtract the same number from each side of an inequality.**

Problem 1: (for Rule 1)

$$14 < 15$$

We can add 10 to both sides of the inequality:

$$14 + \textbf{10} < 15 + \textbf{10}$$
$$24 < 25$$

Problem 2:

$$8 > -3$$

Subtract 2 from both sides of the inequality:

$$8 - \textbf{2} > -3 - \textbf{2}$$
$$6 > -5$$

- -

Rule 2: | **You can multiply or divide each side of an inequality by the same <u>positive</u> number.**

Problem 1: (for Rule 2)

$$6 < 9$$

We can multiply both sides by 2:

$$6 \cdot \textbf{2} < 9 \cdot \textbf{2}$$
$$12 < 18$$

Problem 2:

$$27 > -6$$

Divide both sides by 3:

$$\frac{27}{\textbf{3}} > \frac{-6}{\textbf{3}}$$

$$9 > -2$$

- -

Rule 3: *You can multiply or divide an inequality by a __negative__ number, but you must __change the direction__ of the inequality.*

Problem 1: (for Rule 3)

$$24 > 16$$

We have to change the direction of the inequality from $>$ to $<$ when we multiply by a negative number -2:

$$(24)\,(-2) < (16)\,(-2)$$
$$-48 < -32$$

Problem 2:

$$22 < 33$$

Divide by -11:

$$\frac{22}{-11} > \frac{33}{-11}$$

$$-2 > -3$$

✎ *Exercises*

Apply the three rules above to find the resulting inequality. The first one has been done for you as an example.

1. $4 < 7$ Multiply both sides by 3. $\underline{4 \cdot 3 < 7 \cdot 3, \ 12 < 21}$

2. $10 > -2$ Add -4 to both sides. _____

3. $-3 < -2$ Subtract 10 from both sides. _____

4. $7 < 9$ Multiply both sides by -1. _____

5. $-50 < -10$ Divide both sides by -10. _____

6. $4 > -2$ Divide both sides by -2. _____

7. $8 > 4$ Multiply both sides by -3. _____

8. $-2 > -6$ Multiply both sides by -4. _____

9. $-10 > -11$ Subtract -5 from both sides. _____

10. $-7 < 7$ Add 7 to both sides. _____

5.3 Solving Inequalities—One Step

To solve an inequality, we apply the same procedures as we did for solving equations. Here is an illustration:

$$x + 5 < 8$$

Subtract 5 from both sides of the equation:

$$x + 5 - 5 < 8 - 5$$
$$x < 3$$

The solution to the inequality $x + 5 < 8$ is $x < 3$. What does the solution mean?

The solution consists of all numbers less than 3. It includes 0 and all negative numbers. It includes fractional numbers such as $-\frac{1}{3}$, $\frac{4}{5}$, and $2\frac{1}{4}$; and the decimal numbers -5.7, 0.67, and 2.965. In other words, the solution includes **any type of number** less than 3.

The line above the number line ending with the open dot over 3 shows the solution:

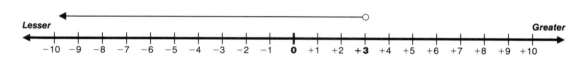

- -

Examine the procedure for solving this inequality:

$$-2a > 12$$

Divide both sides of the inequality by -2:

$$\frac{-2a}{-2} < \frac{12}{-2}$$

Note that the direction of the inequality sign changed, from $>$ to $<$, in accordance with Rule 3 of Section 5.2. Dividing by -2 results in:

$$a < -6$$

which is the solution to the inequality $-2a > 12$. The solution means that all numbers less than -6 will work in the inequality.

On the other hand, here are several numbers that are **not** part of the solution:

$$-5, -2, -0.652, 0, \frac{1}{6}, 3, 10.236$$

The line above the number line with the open dot over -6 shows the solution:

All the examples in this section require one step for solution. In the next lesson we shall look at solving inequalities that require two steps.

EXAMPLES

1. To solve the inequality $s - 8 \leq 6$, add 8 to both sides:

$$s - 8 + \mathbf{8} \leq 6 + \mathbf{8}$$
$$s \leq 14$$

The solution consists of all numbers less than or equal to 14. It includes 14.

2. To solve the inequality $\frac{1}{2}z \geq -3$, multiply both sides by $\frac{2}{1}$ (the coefficient inverted):

$$\frac{1}{2}z \cdot \frac{\mathbf{2}}{\mathbf{1}} \geq -3 \cdot \frac{\mathbf{2}}{\mathbf{1}}$$
$$z \geq -6$$

The solution consists of all numbers greater than or equal to -6. It includes -6.

✎ *Exercises*

For each inequality (in boldface) circle the choices that are part of the solution.

1. $\mathbf{y > 4}$: $-9, \frac{3}{4}, 7, 4.17, -1.7, 100, 5, 3.875$

2. $\mathbf{x \geq -10}$: $-11, 7, 4.555, -10, \frac{1}{7}, -10.43, -9.55, 0$

3. $\mathbf{z \leq 0}$: $-3, -0.222, \frac{4}{9}, 0, 18, -12.83$

Solve.

4. $2r > 6$ _____

5. $s + 8 < 14$ _____

6. $-3w \geq 9$ _____

7. $t - 12 < 9$ _____

8. $-5d > -25$ _____

9. $4a \leq 24$ _____

10. $g + 24 < 0$ _____

5.4 Solving Inequalities—Two Steps

The same procedure applies to solving two-step inequalities as with two-step equations (see Section 2.6). The basic idea is to get the variable by itself. Study this example:

$$2z - 3 > 5$$

Step 1: Add 3 to both sides:

$$2z - 3 + 3 > 5 + 3$$
$$2z > 8$$

Step 2: Divide both sides by 2:

$$\frac{2z}{2} > \frac{8}{2}$$
$$z > 4$$

The solution is $z > 4$.

- -

Here is another example:

$$-4a - 7 < 9$$

To get the variable by itself, there are two steps:

Step 1: Add 7 to both sides:

$$-4a - 7 + 7 < 9 + 7$$
$$-4a < 16$$

Step 2: Divide both sides by -4, and change the direction of the inequality sign from $<$ to $>$:

$$\frac{-4a}{-4} > \frac{16}{-4}$$
$$a > -4$$

The solution is $a > -4$.

✎ Exercises

Use the two-step method to solve these equations.

1. $5x - 1 > 9$ _____

2. $3y + 7 < -2$ _____

3. $-2z - 4 < 12$ _____

4. $\frac{a}{3} + 3 > 4$ _____

5. $-7t - 2 \leq -30$ _____

6. $9m + 7 > 43$ _____

7. $2y - 10 < 20$ _____

5.5 Solving Inequalities— Simplifying Expressions

Solving inequalities may sometimes require simplifying expressions just as we did with equations (Section 4.3). Simplifying means adding and subtracting terms that have the same variable.

The first step simplifies the inequality—if it needs to be simplified. Here is an example:

$$2a + 3a < 25$$

Step 1: Simplify by adding the terms of the left side: $\qquad 5a < 25$

Step 2: Divide both sides by 5: $\qquad\qquad \dfrac{5a}{5} < \dfrac{25}{5}$

$$a < 5$$

The solution is $a < 5$.

- -

Here is another example:

$$4b - 27 > -5b$$

Step 1: Simplify: add $5b$ to both sides

$$4b - 27 + \mathbf{5b} > -5b + \mathbf{5b}$$
$$9b - 27 > 0$$

Step 2: Add 27 to both sides: $\qquad 9b - 27 + \mathbf{27} > 0 + \mathbf{27}$
$$9b > 27$$

Step 3: Divide by 9: $\qquad\qquad \dfrac{9b}{9} > \dfrac{27}{9}$
$$b > 3$$

The solution is $b > 3$.

- -

In this next example:

$$9r \leqq -27$$

the inequality does not need to be simplified. So we go ahead and use the one-step approach:

Step 1: Divide by 9: $\qquad\qquad \dfrac{9r}{9} \leqq \dfrac{-27}{9}$
$$r \leqq -3$$

The solution is $r \leqq -3$.

Remember, the first step is to check to see if the inequality needs to be simplified.

- -

✎ *Exercises*

Solve each inequality.

1. $5g - 3g > 10$ _____

2. $12m + 3m < 30$ _____

3. $6d - 2d + 5 > 29$ _____

4. $11x > 55$ _____

5. $3y < 2y + 17$ _____

6. $2z - 12 > -10$ _____

7. $4t - 8 < 2t - 2$ _____

5.6 Chapter 5 Review

Which of these are inequalities? Mark the inequalities with an **I**.

1. $6 = 14$ _____

2. $17 > 9$ _____

3. $-4 < 6$ _____

4. $10 \geqq -12$ _____

5. $8 + 6$ _____

6. $13 = 12 + 1$ _____

Perform each operation to find the resulting inequality.

7. $2 < 3$ Multiply each side by 4. _____

8. $4 > -1$ Add 3 to each side. _____

9. $10 > 9$ Multiply each side by -1. _____

10. $-3 < -2$ Subtract 2 from each side. _____

11. $50 > 25$ Divide each side by -5. _____

Solve each inequality.

12. $4x > 16$ _____

13. $3y - 10 < 20$ _____

14. $4r - 2r > 6 - r$ _____

15. $6t + 4 + 3t < 40$ _____

16. $5s - 17 + 3s > 15$ _____

6. *Factoring*

6.1 Introduction to Factoring

What is factoring in algebra? Factoring is the process of "breaking up" a product. For example, you can "break up" 15 as a product of 5 and 3:

$$15 = 5 \cdot 3$$

The numbers 5 and 3 are called **factors** of 15. We factored 15 into 5 and 3. We could also factor 15 into 1 and 15; or -5 and -3; or -1 and -15 because

$$15 = 1 \cdot 15$$
$$15 = (-5)(-3)$$
$$15 = (-1)(-15)$$

- -

In the same way we factor a term such as $2x$ into factors 2 and x:

$$2x = 2 \cdot x$$

We can factor the term $7r^2$ in three different ways:

$$7r^2 = 7 \cdot r^2$$
$$7r^2 = 7 \cdot r \cdot r$$
$$7r^2 = 7r \cdot r$$

From this example, we see that a term can be factored in more than one way. We also see that we can have more than two factors.

EXAMPLES

1. The number 24 can be factored in many ways. Here are some of the ways:

$$24 = 8 \cdot 3$$
$$24 = (-6)(-4)$$
$$24 = 24 \cdot 1$$
$$24 = (-6)(-2)(2)$$
$$24 = 2 \cdot 2 \cdot 2 \cdot 3$$

2. Here are some of the ways the term $4z^3$ can be factored:

$$4z^3 = 4 \cdot z^3$$
$$4z^3 = 4 \cdot z^2 \cdot z$$
$$4z^3 = 4 \cdot z \cdot z \cdot z$$
$$4z^3 = 2 \cdot 2 \cdot z^3$$
$$4z^3 = 2 \cdot 2 \cdot z^2 \cdot z$$
$$4z^3 = 2 \cdot 2 \cdot z \cdot z \cdot z$$

Factor each number or term at least two ways.

1. 18 _____ **4.** $3xy$ _____

2. $7s^2$ _____ **5.** 25 _____

3. $9r$ _____ **6.** $23t^2$ _____

Each group shows several factors of a term. Find the term.

7. 2, 3, d _____ **10.** z, 5, 2, z^2, 8 _____

8. 5, x^2, x _____ **11.** 6, 4, s, r^3 _____

9. 3, 7, 2, y, y, y _____

6.2 *Finding the Greatest Common Factor*

In this section we will factor polynomials, using the main idea of the previous section. That idea is that factoring is the process of breaking up a number, term, or polynomial.

Problem 1:

$$3x + 6y$$

In this binomial, notice that both terms can be divided by 3:

$$\frac{3x + 6y}{3}$$

Divide each term by 3:　　$\dfrac{3x}{3} = x$

$$\dfrac{6y}{3} = 2y$$

Combine the two results:　　$\dfrac{3x + 6y}{3} = x + 2y$

So the binomial $3x + 6y$ can be broken up into the factors 3 and $x + 2y$:

$$3x + 6y = (3)\,(x + 2y)$$

To factor a polynomial, start by looking for a term common to all the terms of the polynomial. In the example above this common term, or **common factor**, is 3.

- -

Problem 2:

$$8z^2 - 32z$$

Ask: what term divides both $8z^2$ and $-32z$? First, we see that 8 is common to both 8 and -32. Then we find that z is common to both z^2 and z. So we put these pieces together to get $8z$ as the common factor dividing both $8z^2$ and $-32z$.

$$\frac{8z^2 - 32z}{8z}$$

Divide each term by $8z$:　　$\dfrac{8z^2}{8z} = z$

$$\dfrac{-32z}{8z} = -4$$

Combine these results:　　$z - 4$

The factors of $8z^2 - 32z$ are $8z$ and $z - 4$:

$$8z^2 - 32z = (8z)\,(z - 4)$$

- -

Problem 3:

When we search for a common factor that divides each term of a polynomial, we seek the largest factor, also known as the **greatest common factor**. For example, in this binomial:

$$30y^2 + 45y$$

the term $5y$ divides each term of $30y + 45y$. But $5y$ is not the greatest factor that is common to $30y$ and $45y$. The term $15y$ is. Since $15y$ is the greatest common factor, we use it as one of the factors.

Dividing both terms by $15y$, we get

$$\frac{30y^2 + 45y}{15y} = 2y + 3$$

The factors of $30y^2 + 45y$ are $15y$ and $2y + 3$.

- -

Problem 4:

Our three examples above have all been with binomials. This example deals with a trinomial:

$$12x^3 + 24x^2 - 36x$$

Although $2x$, $4x$ and $6x$ divide each term of the trinomial, the **greatest** common factor is $12x$. Divide each term by $12x$:

$$\frac{12x^3 + 24x^2 - 36x}{12x} = x^2 + 2x - 3$$

The factors are $12x$ and $x^2 + 2x - 3$.

Remember, always use the **greatest** common factor as one of the factors.

✎ *Exercises*

Find the factors and write them as a product. Make sure the common factor in each is the greatest common factor.

1. $7s + 7$ _____

2. $11t - 22$ _____

3. $9q^2 - 36$ _____

4. $xy - xz$ _____

5. $4a^2 - 36a$ _____

6. $b^3v + b^2v$ _____

7. $25r^3 + 75r$ _____

8. $250 - 1000m$ _____

9. $rs^2t + r^2st$ _____

10. $5w^2 - 10w + 20$ _____

6.3 *Multiplying Two Special Binomials*

To get ready for the next section, which deals with factoring the difference of two squares, we first need to look at how certain pairs of binomials known as "special binomials" are multiplied. Take a look at this example:

$$(x + 3)(x - 3) = ?$$

The two special binomials are the sum $(x + 3)$ and the difference $(x - 3)$ of the same two numbers x and 3. We call the binomials $(x + 3)$ and $(x - 3)$ **special binomials** because of their connection to each other.

We multiply these two binomials in vertical form:

$$
\begin{array}{r}
x + 3 \\
x - 3 \\
\hline
\end{array}
$$

	$x + 3$
	$x - 3$
Multiply -3 times $x + 3$:	$-\,3x - 9$
Multiply x times $x + 3$:	$x^2 + 3x$
Add:	$x^2 +\ \ 0 - 9$

The product of the two binomials is $x^2 - 9$. Or, in horizontal form:

$$(x + 3)(x - 3) = x^2 - 9$$

The product is the same as the difference of the squares of x and 3.

- -

This second example shows the same connection between the two special binomials:

$$(a + b)(a - b)$$

Again, we have the sum $(a + b)$ and the difference $(a - b)$ of two numbers.

Here is the vertical multiplication:

	$a + b$
	$a - b$
Multiply $-b$ times $a + b$:	$-\,ab - b^2$
Multiply a times $a + b$:	$a^2 + ab$
Adding:	$a^2 +\ \ 0 - b^2$

The product is $a^2 - b^2$, the difference of the squares of a and b.

- -

The two examples above illustrate the following rule:

The product of the sum and the difference of the same two numbers equals the difference of the squares of the numbers.

You'll probably find it easier to remember the rule when it's written in mathematical form:

$$(a+b)(a-b) = a^2 - b^2$$

EXAMPLES

We use the rule above to find these products:

1. $(y + 5)(y - 5) = y^2 - 5^2 = y^2 - 25$

2. $(z - 7)(z + 7) = z^2 - 7^2 = z^2 - 49$

3. $(6 - t)(6 + t) = 6^2 - t^2 = 36 - t^2$

4. $(r + s)(r - s) = r^2 - s^2$

5. $(11 - q)(11 + q) = 11^2 - q^2 = 121 - q^2$

6. $(p - q)(p + q) = p^2 - q^2$

7. $(3x + y)(3x - y) = (3x)^2 - y^2 = 3^2x^2 - y^2 = 9x^2 - y^2$

✎ *Exercises*

Use the rule of this section to find the products.

1. $(a + 3)(a - 3) = $ _____

2. $(s + 6)(s - 6) = $ _____

3. $(7 - w)(7 + w) = $ _____

4. $(b - 10)(b + 10) = $ _____

5. $(e + f)(e - f) = $ _____

6. $(t + 8)(t - 8) = $ _____

7. $(r + 3m)(r - 3m) = $ _____

6.4 The Difference of Two Squares

In Lesson 6.3 we found that

$$(x + 3)(x - 3) = x^2 - 9$$

The expression $x^2 - 9$ is the difference of x^2 and 3^2, the difference of two squares.

We can write the equation above "backwards" as

$$x^2 - 9 = (x + 3)(x - 3)$$

In this form, we recognize that $x + 3$ and $x - 3$ are **factors** of $x^2 - 9$.

- -

Here is a second example:

$$(a - 5)(a + 5) = a^2 - 25$$

If we write the equation backwards, we get

$$a^2 - 25 = (a + 5)(a - 5)$$

From this last equation we see that the factors of $a^2 - 25$ are $(a + 5)$ and $(a - 5)$. The left-hand side of the equation shows the difference of two squares. These two examples illustrate how to factor the difference of two squares.

- -

Here are two steps to use when factoring the difference of two squares:

Step 1. Find the square root of each term.
For the example

$$y^2 - 25$$

the square root of y^2 is y, and the square root of 25 is 5.

Step 2. Put together the two factors:

Factor 1: the **sum** of the square roots: $y + 5$
Factor 2: the **difference** of the square roots: $y - 5$

$$y^2 - 25 = (y + 5)(y - 5)$$

- -

EXAMPLES

We use the two steps above to factor the difference of two squares.

1. $w^2 - 36 = ?$

    Step 1: w is the square root of w^2, and 6 is the square root of 36.

    Step 2: Factor 1: $w + 6$
                  Factor 2: $w - 6$

The factors of $w^2 - 36$ are $w + 6$ and $w - 6$:

$$w^2 - 36 = (w + 6)(w - 6)$$

2. $r^2 - 49 = ?$

    Step 1: r is the square root of r^2, and 7 is the square root of 49.

    Step 2: $r^2 - 49 = (r + 7)(r - 7)$

3. $4 - a^2 = ?$

    Step 1: 2 is the square root of 4, and a is the square root of a^2.

    Step 2: $4 - a^2 = (2 + a)(2 - a)$

4. $49m^2 - 25 = ?$

    Step 1: The square root of $49m^2$ is $7m$. We get this answer by taking the square roots of 49 and of m^2, and then multiplying the answers together. The square root of 25 is 5.

    Step 2: $49m^2 - 25 = (7m + 5)(7m - 5)$

✎ *Exercises*

Use the steps outlined above to factor each of these differences of two squares.

1. $x^2 - 16 = $ _____

2. $y^2 - 81 = $ _____

3. $z^2 - 100 = $ _____

4. $9 - q^2 = $ _____

5. $1 - b^2 = $ _____

6. $a^2 - b^2 = $ _____

7. $100w^2 - 81 = $ _____

6.5 *Factoring Trinomials*

How do you factor a trinomial that does not contain any common factor? For example:

$$x^2 + 5x + 6$$

We start by assuming that the trinomial is the product of two binomials:

$$(? + ?)(? + ?) = x^2 + 5x + 6$$

where the question marks stand for a variable or a number. These two binomials are the factors of the trinomial.

- -

Now think back to the **FOIL** method of horizontal multiplication. (Review it in Lesson 4.11 if you need to.) Remember:

> **F** stands for first terms
> **O** stands for outside terms
> **I** stands for inside terms
> **L** stands for last terms

So, in the trinomial that we are factoring:

> x^2 is the product of the first terms of the factors (**F**)
> $5x$ comes from adding the products of the outside (**O**) and inside (**I**) terms (**O** + **I**)
> 6 is the product of the last terms of the factors (**L**)

This information gives us the following three steps:

Step 1: **F** stands for first. Break up the first term of the trinomial, x^2, into $x \cdot x$. Write these x's down as the first terms of the two factors:

$$(x + ?)(x + ?) = x^2 + 5x + 6$$

Step 2: Next, we skip to **L**, the last term of the trinomial. It is 6. What two numbers multiply to produce 6? Here are all the possibilities:

> 1 and 6
> −1 and −6
> 3 and 2
> −3 and −2

As you see, there are several choices. Fortunately, we can eliminate two of them right away—the ones with the negative signs. The middle term (**O** + **I**) of the trinomial is positive—and so the factors have to be positive.

This leaves us with two choices:

> 1 and 6
> 3 and 2

We cannot decide on the correct one until we go to Step 3.

Step 3: The correct choices for the last terms will be the pair of numbers whose <u>sum</u> (**O** + **I** in **FOIL**) is 5—the coefficient of the middle term of the trinomial.

If you add the pairs in Step 2, you will find that only the pair 3 and 2 add up to 5. So:

$$(x + 3)(x + 2) = x^2 + 5x + 6$$

Or, to write it in the way that is customary when factoring a trinomial:

$$x^2 + 5x + 6 = (x + 3)(x + 2)$$

Check your answer by multiplying $(x + 3)(x + 2)$. The answer will be $x^2 + 5x + 6$.

The order in which you write the two binomials doesn't matter. The last equation, above, can also be written:

$$x^2 + 5x + 6 = (x + 2)(x + 3)$$

✎ *Exercises*

Factor each trinomial into binomial factors.

1. $a^2 + 8a + 7$ _____

2. $x^2 + 14x + 13$ _____

3. $y^2 + 8y + 15$ _____

4. $m^2 + 7m + 10$ _____

5. $t^2 + 7t + 12$ _____

6. $t^2 + 8t + 12$ _____

7. $t^2 + 13t + 12$ _____

6.6 Factoring Trinomials Containing a Negative

In the last lesson, you learned how to factor a trinomial containing only positive numbers:

$$x^2 + 5x + 6 = (x + 2)(x + 3)$$

Now let's make one change. Suppose the **middle term** of the trinomial is **negative** instead of positive:

$$x^2 - 5x + 6 = ?$$

How do you factor this?

Step 1: Since we know that the product of the first (**F**) terms of the factors will be x^2, we can write:

$$x^2 - 5x + 6 = (x \quad)(x \quad)$$

Step 2: The product of the last (**L**) terms of the factors equals 6. The possibilities, again, are:

$$\begin{array}{rcl} 1 & \text{and} & 6 \\ -1 & \text{and} & -6 \\ 3 & \text{and} & 2 \\ -3 & \text{and} & -2 \end{array}$$

Notice this time, however, that the middle term of the trinomial is negative. Therefore, we can eliminate the positive pairs 1, 6 and 3, 2. The only possibilities that fit the trinomial are negative:

$$\begin{array}{rcl} -1 & \text{and} & -6 \\ -3 & \text{and} & -2 \end{array}$$

Step 3: The combination that adds to the coefficient of the middle term (-5) is -3 (**O**) and -2 (**I**):

$$x^2 - 5x + 6 = (x - 2)(x - 3)$$

The factors of $x^2 - 5x + 6$ are $(x - 2)$ and $(x - 3)$.

- -

Here is another example using these three steps:

Factor this trinomial:

$$y^2 - 7y + 10$$

Step 1: Since we know that the product of the first (**F**) terms of the factors will be y^2, we can write:

$$y^2 - 7y + 10 = (y \quad)(y \quad)$$

Step 2: The product of the last (**L**) terms of the factors equals 10. Since the middle term of the trinomial is negative, the only possibilities are:

$$\begin{array}{rcl} -1 & \text{and} & -10 \\ -5 & \text{and} & -2 \end{array}$$

Step 3: The combination that adds to the coefficient of the middle term (-7) is -5 (**O**) and -2 (**I**):

$$y^2 - 7y + 10 = (y - 2)(y - 5)$$

The factors of $y^2 - 7y + 10$ are $(y - 2)$ and $(y - 5)$.

- -

In both this lesson and in Lesson 6.5, the last term of each trinomial was positive. This leads us to the following rule whenever you are factoring a trinomial with a **positive last term:**

If the trinomial's <u>middle term</u> is also <u>positive</u>, then the terms of its binomial factors are linked by <u>plus</u> signs:

$$x^2 + 3x + 2 = (x + 2)(x + 1)$$

If the trinomial's <u>middle term</u> is <u>negative</u>, then the terms of its binomial factors are linked by <u>minus</u> signs:

$$x^2 - 3x + 2 = (x - 2)(x - 1)$$

Notice that this rule only applies when the **last** term of the trinomial is **positive.**

✎ Exercises

Factor each trinomial into binomial factors.

1. $a^2 + 4a + 4$ _____

2. $b^2 + 4b + 3$ _____

3. $s^2 - 10s + 21$ _____

4. $q^2 - 8q + 15$ _____

5. $m^2 - 9m + 14$ _____

6. $r^2 + 8r + 12$ _____

6.7 More Factoring Trinomials Containing a Negative

In the last two lessons, you factored trinomials with a **positive** last term. You found that if the trinomial's middle term is negative, then the terms of its binomial factors are linked by minus signs. And if the trinomial's middle term is positive, then the terms of its binomial factors are linked by plus signs.

Now what about trinomials with a **negative** last term? For example:

    1. $x^2 + x - 6$
    2. $x^2 - x - 6$

The binomial factors of these trinomials contain different signs—one plus, the other minus. Look at the factors carefully. They are worked out for you. Use the **FOIL** method to multiply each pair of factors to see how the trinomial is their product.

    1. $x^2 + x - 6 = (x + 3)(x - 2)$
    2. $x^2 - x - 6 = (x - 3)(x + 2)$

- -

Let's apply the three-step factoring method to Equation 1 to see how we factor it:

Step 1: The same as usual. Break up the first term (**F**) of the trinomial into $x \cdot x$:

$$x^2 + x - 6 = (x \quad)(x \quad)$$

Step 2: Again, the same as usual. We list all possible pairs whose product (**L**) is the last term of the trinomial. Remember: since that last term is negative (-6), one number of the pair has to be positive and the other negative:

$$+1 \text{ and } -6$$
$$-1 \text{ and } +6$$
$$+3 \text{ and } -2$$
$$-3 \text{ and } +2$$

Step 3: To find the coefficient (1) of the middle term (x) of the trinomial, add the choices you listed in Step 2. You'll find that only one pair passes the test:

$$+3 \text{ and } -2$$

Therefore:

$$x^2 + x - 6 = (x + 3)(x - 2)$$

- -

Here's the three-step method applied to Equation 2 at the beginning of the lesson:

Step 1: $\qquad\qquad\qquad\qquad x^2 - x - 6 = (x \qquad) (x \qquad)$

Step 2: $\qquad\qquad\qquad\qquad\qquad\qquad$ $+ 1$ and -6
$\qquad\qquad\qquad\qquad\qquad\qquad\qquad\qquad$ -1 and $+6$
$\qquad\qquad\qquad\qquad\qquad\qquad\qquad\qquad$ $+3$ and -2
$\qquad\qquad\qquad\qquad\qquad\qquad\qquad\qquad$ -3 and $+2$

Notice that Steps 1 and 2 are exactly the same as in the earlier example in this lesson. But Step 3 has different results:

Step 3: The coefficient of the middle term is a negative number (-1). So the pair that passes the addition test is:

$$-3 \text{ and } +2$$

Therefore:

$$x^2 - x - 6 = (x - 3)(x + 2)$$

Reread this lesson carefully to make sure you understand it.

✎ *Exercises*

Factor each trinomial into binomial factors. (Be careful of the signs! Some are put in to trick you.)

1. $x^2 - x - 12$ _____

2. $y^2 + 6y - 7$ _____

3. $z^2 + 5z + 6$ _____

4. $a^2 - 6a - 7$ _____

5. $b^2 + b - 12$ _____

6. $c^2 - 5c + 6$ _____

6.8 Factoring More Difficult Trinomials

If the coefficient of the first term of a trinomial such as

$$4x^2 + 16x + 15$$

is not 1, then factoring the trinomial can be difficult. This section shows three examples of this type. They illustrate the need to use trial and error in factoring when there are many possible combinations. They also show the traps that await you.

Problem 1. $2z^2 + 5z + 3 = (? + ?)(? + ?)$

1. Break $2z^2$ into $2z$ and z:

$$2z^2 + 5z + 3 = (2z + ?)(z + ?)$$

2. Break 3 into:

1 and 3
3 and 1
-1 and -3
-3 and -1

3. Ask yourself which combination from **2** replaces the question marks in:

$$2z^2 + 5z + 3 = (2z + ?)(z + ?)$$

4. Often the best way to do this is to experiment—trial and error. Fortunately, we can eliminate the last two combinations, the ones with negative signs, right away. The last term and the middle term of the trinomial are both positive. Therefore there are no negatives in the factors.

This leaves us with two possibilities:

$$(2z + 1)(z + 3)$$

and

$$(2z + 3)(z + 1)$$

Let's try the first one. Use **FOIL** to multiply. You get:

$$(2z + 1)(z + 3) = 2z^2 + 7z + 3$$

The middle term of the product is $7z$. This is not what we want. So the pair 1 and 3 does not work.

Let's try again, reversing the order of the numbers: 3 and 1. Again multiply, using **FOIL**:

$$(2z + 3)(z + 1) = 2z^2 + 5z + 3$$

This works. The factors are $(2z + 3)$ and $(z + 1)$.

- -

Problem 2. $6w^2 - 7w + 2 = (? + ?)(? + ?)$

This at first looks like a hard example. Remember the quick tricks of Lesson 6.6 that will help us cut down on the number of choices before we begin:

● The middle term of the trinomial $(-7w)$ is negative. Therefore, there must also be a negative in at least one of the factors—and maybe in both.

● Look at the last term of the trinomial $(+2)$. It's positive. Now this number is the product of the two last terms in the factors (**L** in **FOIL**). Since we know that one of these numbers is negative, both must be (negative times negative equals positive).

The factors of the trinomial, then, must have the form:

$$(? - ?)(? - ?)$$

Now we are ready to try factoring the trinomial:

$$6w^2 - 7w + 2 = (? - ?)(? - ?)$$

1. List the possible factors of the first term. They are:

$$6w \text{ and } w$$
$$3w \text{ and } 2w$$

2. List all the possible factors of the last term. Here there is only one possiblity: -2 and -1. But we don't know what order the numbers go in:

$$-2 \text{ and } -1, \text{ or}$$
$$-1 \text{ and } -2$$

3. Now we can list all possible combinations of factors for our trinomial:

$$\left.\begin{matrix}(6w - 2)(w - 1) \\ (6w - 1)(w - 2)\end{matrix}\right\}\ \left\{\begin{matrix}\text{Same terms, but order} \\ \text{of second terms is reversed}\end{matrix}\right.$$

$$\left.\begin{matrix}(3w - 2)(2w - 1) \\ (3w - 1)(2w - 2)\end{matrix}\right\}\ \left\{\begin{matrix}\text{Same terms, but order} \\ \text{of second terms is reversed}\end{matrix}\right.$$

4. This is the part that takes time. We do the multiplication for the middle term (**O** + **I**) of each possible set of factors. Only one gives us $-7w$:

$$6w^2 - 7w + 2 = (3w - 2)(2w - 1)$$

So the factors of $6w^2 - 7w + 2$ are $(3w - 2)$ and $(2w - 1)$.

- -

Problem 3. $4y^2 + 16y + 15$

1. Break $4y^2$ into:

$$4y \text{ and } y$$
$$2y \text{ and } 2y$$

2. Break 15 into:

$$5 \text{ and } 3$$
$$3 \text{ and } 5$$
$$1 \text{ and } 15$$
$$15 \text{ and } 1$$

(Notice that since there is no negative middle term in the trinomial, and since the last term is also positive, we don't have to bother with negatives in the factors.)

3. Here are all the possibilities:

$$(4y + 5)(y + 3) \qquad (2y + 5)(2y + 3)$$
$$(4y + 3)(y + 5) \qquad (2y + 3)(2y + 5)$$

$$(4y + 1)(y + 15) \qquad (2y + 1)(2y + 15)$$
$$(4y + 15)(y + 1) \qquad (2y + 15)(2y + 1)$$

4. Once again, trial and error is the way we find the correct factors. After several trials (and errors!) we find that the combination that works is $2y$ and $2y$ together with 3 and 5:

$$(2y + 3)(2y + 5) = 4y^2 + 16y + 15$$

Is there any shortcut to factoring all these types of trinomials? Unfortunately, no. If there is any trick at all, it's the art of juggling two sets of factors to get the **middle** term of the trinomial.

✎ *Exercises*

Factor each trinomial into binomial factors.

1. $7c^2 + 9c + 2$ _____

2. $2x^2 + 9x + 4$ _____

3. $2y^2 - 5y + 3$ _____

4. $10z^2 - 3z - 1$ _____

5. $6t^2 - 7t - 5$ _____

6. $5s^2 - 4s - 12$ _____

6.9 Complete Factoring

This final section on factoring combines three types of factoring:

      1. Finding the greatest common factor (see Lesson 6.2)
      2. The difference of two squares (see Lesson 6.4)
      3. Factoring trinomials (see Lessons 6.5–6.8)

When we apply all possible ways to factor an expression, the process is called **complete factoring**. Our first example is a trinomial:

$$2x^3 + 12x^2 + 16x$$

There are two steps to factoring this trinomial completely. These steps use methods 1. and 3. above.

Step 1: Ask: is there a monomial common to all three terms of the trinomial?

The answer is yes—the greatest monomial factor is $2x$:

$$(2x)(x^2 + 6x + 8)$$

We have now factored the original trinomial into two factors: $(2x)$ and $(x^2 + 6x + 8)$.

Step 2: Now ask: how can we factor the trinomial $(x^2 + 6x + 8)$?

To answer this question, write the trinomial into its unknown factors:

$$(x^2 + 6x + 8) = (? + ?)(? + ?)$$

and use the rule of Section 6.6:

1. Break x^2 into $x \cdot x$:

$$x^2 + 6x + 8 = (x + ?)(x + ?)$$

2. Here are the possibilities for the last terms of the factors:

4 and 2
1 and 8

Remember: The last term of the trinomial is positive. So we can eliminate any negative factors (like -4 or -2), because the middle term of the trinomial is also positive.

3. Ask: which combination will add to the coefficient of the middle term (6)?

The answer is 4 and 2:

$$x^2 + 6x + 8 = (x + 4)(x + 2)$$

Now we can put together the three factors:

$$2x^3 + 12x^2 + 16x = (2x)(x + 4)(x + 2)$$

Follow the two steps outlined above to factor a trinomial completely.

- -

Our second example involves a binomial:

$$3a^3 - 27a$$

Our procedure for this binomial also has two steps. These two steps come from methods 1. and 2. referred to at the beginning of this section.

Step 1: Ask: is there a common monomial that can be factored from the binomial?

The answer is yes, and the greatest common monomial is $3a$:

$$3a^3 - 27a = (3a)\,(a^2 - 9)$$

Step 2: Ask: can the binomial $(a^2 - 9)$ be factored?

The answer is yes because $(a^2 - 9)$ is the difference of two squares:

$$a^2 - 9 = (a + 3)\,(a - 3)$$

The complete factoring of $3a^2 - 27a$ is:

$$3a^3 - 27a = (3a)\,(a + 3)\,(a - 3)$$

EXAMPLES

1. $3z^2 + 9z + 6$

Step 1: The greatest common monomial is 3:

$$3z^2 + 9z + 6 = (3)\,(z^2 + 3z + 2)$$

Step 2: The trinomial $z^2 + 3z + 2$ has factors $(z + 2)\,(z + 1)$.

The complete factoring of $3z^2 + 9z + 6$ is:

$$3z^2 + 9z + 6 = (3)\,(z + 2)\,(z + 1)$$

2. $25y^3 - 100y$

Step 1: The greatest common monomial is $25y$:

$$25y^3 - 100y = (25y)\,(y^2 - 4)$$

Step 2: $(y^2 - 4)$ can be factored by the difference of two squares:

$$(y^2 - 4) = (y + 2)\,(y - 2)$$

The complete factoring of $25y^3 - 100y$ is:

$$25y^3 - 100y = (25y)\,(y + 2)\,(y - 2)$$

Use the procedures outlined above to factor each of the following completely.

1. $2x^2 - 2$ _____

2. $3y^2 + 9y + 6$ _____

3. $3t^2 - 36t + 105$ _____

4. $10f^2 - 5f - 50$ _____

5. $2s^2 - 72$ _____

6. $2x^3 - 26x^2 + 72x$ _____

7. $100s^2 - 400$ _____

8. $6b^3 - 9b^2 - 15b$ _____

9. $9x^3 - 81x$ _____

10. $24z^3 - 14z^2 + 2z$ _____

6.10 Zero Products

In the next section you will learn how to solve equations by using the factoring methods of this chapter. First you need to learn a law of arithmetic that will help in the next section.

In arithmetic you learned that if you multiply any number by 0, the product is 0. For instance,

$$26 \cdot 0 = 0$$

$$\frac{3}{5} \cdot 0 = 0$$

$$0 \cdot -327 = 0$$

- -

But what if you didn't know one of the numbers? Suppose

$$k \cdot 19 = 0$$

where k is a number. What can you say about k? Yes, it has to be 0 because

$$0 \cdot 19 = 0$$

Suppose we had the equation

$$-56 \cdot q = 0$$

where q is a number. What can you conclude about q? Since the product of the two numbers is 0, then q must be 0.

- -

What if the equation looks like this, with two variables:

$$p \cdot q = 0$$

where p and q are numbers? In this case we do not know either p or q. But the product of these numbers is 0.

What conclusion can we draw from this equation? That either p must be 0, or q must be 0, or that both must be 0. This leads to this law of arithmetic:

> **If the product of two numbers equals 0, then at least one of them must be 0.**

1. If $5 \cdot z = 0$ then $z = 0$.

2. If $a \cdot \dfrac{5}{8} = 0$ then $a = 0$.

3. If $-216 \cdot d = 0$ then $d = 0$.

4. If $r \cdot s = 0$ then $r = 0$ or $s = 0$ or both r and s equal 0.

✎ Exercises

1. If $5 \cdot w = 0$, then $w =$ _____

2. If $t \cdot -3 = 0$, then $t =$ _____

3. If $m \cdot n = 0$, then what can you say about m and n? _____

6.11 Solving Equations by Factoring

How can we apply the techniques of factoring to solve equations?

For example, for the equation

$$x^2 - 9 = 0$$

the left-hand side is a binomial. This binomial is the difference of two squares. In Section 6.4 we learned how to factor the difference of two squares.

The binomial $x^2 - 9$ can be factored into two factors as follows:

$$x^2 - 9 = (x + 3)(x - 3)$$

When we replace $x^2 - 9$ with these two factors in the equation

$$x^2 - 9 = 0$$

it becomes

$$(x + 3)(x - 3) = 0$$

This last equation is the product of two factors equaling 0.

In Lesson 6.10 we learned that if the product of two numbers equals 0, then at least one of them has to be 0. From this law of arithmetic, we conclude that either

$$(x + 3) = 0 \quad \text{or}$$

$$(x - 3) = 0$$

Solving both of these, we have

$$
\begin{array}{ll}
& x + 3 = 0 \\
\text{Subtract 3:} & \underline{-3 \quad -3} \\
& x = -3
\end{array}
\qquad
\begin{array}{ll}
& x - 3 = 0 \\
\text{Add 3:} & \underline{+3 \quad +3} \\
& x = 3
\end{array}
$$

When $x = -3$, the factor $(x + 3)$ equals 0, and when $x = 3$, the factor $(x - 3)$ equals 0.

The solutions of the equation $x^2 - 9 = 0$ are -3 and 3.

- -

Our factoring techniques allow us to factor special equations. These equations must satisfy two conditions. First, the highest **exponent** of the variable of these equations must be 2, such as in

$$q^2 - 12q + 36 = 0$$

A second condition that must exist is that these equations can be factored.

For the equation above we illustrate how to use factoring to solve equations that have these conditions. This example is a trinomial.

The highest exponent of the variable q is 2. Now we use Lesson 6.6 to factor the trinomial.

$$q^2 - 12q + 36 = (q - 9)(q - 4)$$

The original equation becomes

$$(q - 9)(q - 4) = 0$$

This last equation is the product of two factors that equals 0. The law of arithmetic of Lesson 6.10 tells us that either one of these factors must be 0.

Add 9:
$$\begin{aligned} q - 9 &= 0 \\ +9 \quad &+9 \\ \hline q &= 9 \end{aligned}$$

Add 4:
$$\begin{aligned} q - 4 &= 0 \\ +4 \quad &+4 \\ \hline q &= 4 \end{aligned}$$

The solutions are 9 and 4.

- -

Equations such as the two that we solved

$$x^2 - 9 = 0 \quad \text{and}$$
$$q^2 - 12q + 36 = 0$$

have a special name. They are called **quadratic equations**. A quadratic equation is an equation with only **one** variable, and its highest exponent is **2**.

Here are some examples of quadratic equations:

$$s^2 - 6s + 9 = 0$$

$$t^2 + 4t - 13 = 0$$

$$y^2 - 117 = 0$$

These are **not** quadratic equations:

$$a - 5 = 0 \text{ (the highest exponent is less than 2)}$$

$$c^3 + c^2 - c + 22 = 0 \text{ (the highest exponent is more than 2)}$$

$$x^2 - 5y + 19 = 0 \text{ (there are two variables)}$$

Some quadratic equations—but not all—can be solved by factoring.

- -

EXAMPLES

1. We solve $s^2 - 13s + 42 = 0$ by factoring:

$$s^2 - 13s + 42 = (s - 7)(s - 6) = 0$$

Therefore, $s - 7 = 0$ or $s - 6 = 0$, and the solutions are 7 and 6.

2. To solve $z^2 - z - 20 = 0$, we factor the trinomial: $z^2 - z - 20 = (z - 5)$ $(z + 4)$. Then

$$z - 5 = 0 \quad \text{or}$$
$$z + 4 = 0$$

leading to $z = 5$ or $z = -4$.

3. The equation $6w^2 - 7w + 2 = 0$ can be solved by factoring

$$6w^2 - 7w + 2 = 0$$
$$(3w - 2)(2w - 1) = 0$$

Set each factor equal to zero and solve:

Factor 1:   Add 2 to both sides:

$$\begin{array}{rr} 3w - 2 = & 0 \\ +2 & +2 \\ \hline 3w = & 2 \end{array}$$

Divide by 3: $w = \dfrac{2}{3}$

Factor 2:   Add 1 to both sides:

$$\begin{array}{rr} 2w - 1 = & 0 \\ +1 & +1 \\ \hline 2w = & 1 \end{array}$$

Divide by 2: $w = \dfrac{1}{2}$

The solutions are $\dfrac{1}{2}$ and $\dfrac{2}{3}$.

✎ Exercises

Solve each of these equations by factoring.

1. $x^2 - 100 = 0$ _____

2. $y^2 - 5y + 4 = 0$ _____

3. $2z^2 - z - 10 = 0$ _____

4. $5q^2 + 6q - 8 = 0$ _____

5. $s^2 - 4 = 0$ _____

6. $r^2 + 10r + 24 = 0$ _____

7. $21m^2 - 10m + 1 = 0$ _____

8. $t^2 - 49 = 0$ _____

Put a checkmark next to the equations that are quadratic equations.

9. $z^2 + 14z - 12 = 0$ _____

10. $x^2 + y^2 = 0$ _____

11. $q^2 - 24 = 0$ _____

12. $14a^2 - 10a^3 + 85 = 0$ _____

13. $13w^3 - 27 = 0$ _____

14. $3r^2 + 5s - 13 = 0$ _____

15. $p^2 - 125 = 0$ _____

6.12 Chapter 6 Review

Find the greatest monomial factor for each of these expressions. Write the factors as products.

1. $13x - 13$ _____

2. $3y^3 - 9y + 27y^2$ _____

3. $20z^2 - 60$ _____

4. $16a^3 + 36a^2 - 48a$ _____

5. $c^3d + c^2d^2$ _____

Multiply.

6. $(x + 7)(x - 7) =$ _____

7. $(s - 10)(s + 10) =$ _____

8. $(y + z)(y - z) =$ _____

9. $(8 - w)(8 + w) =$ _____

Factor using the method of the difference of two squares.

10. $x^2 - 36 =$ _____

11. $y^2 - 100 =$ _____

12. $p^2 - q^2 =$ _____

13. $81 - z^2 =$ _____

Multiply.

14. $(x + 3)(x - 7) =$ _____

15. $(2y + 7)(3y - 10) =$ _____

16. $(3w - 4)(5w - 6) =$ _____

17. $(8a + 2)(7a + 9) =$ _____

Factor into binomial factors.

18. $x^2 + 10x + 21$ _____

19. $y^2 - 7y + 10$ _____

20. $2z^2 + 17z + 8$ _____

21. $3s^2 - 11s + 10$ _____

Factor each of the following completely.

22. $5x^3 - 125x$ _____

23. $2x^2 + 10x + 12$ _____

24. $8x^3 - 28x^2 + 24x$ _____

25. $32 - 2a^2$ _____

Solve the following equations.

26. $(x + 2)(x - 3) = 0$ _____

27. $x(x + 7) = 0$ _____

28. $x^2 - 5x = 0$ _____

29. $4x^2 - 25 = 0$ _____

30. $x^2 + 10x + 21 = 0$ (See your answer to No. 18) _____

31. $3s^2 - 11s + 10 = 0$ (See your answer to No. 21) _____

32. $5x^3 - 125x = 0$ (See your answer to No. 22. HINT: There are 3 sets of factors, so there will be 3 answers to the problem.) _____

33. $8x^3 - 28x^2 + 24x$ (See your answer to No. 24.) _____